RECLAIM
& UNLEASH

YOUR VIP POWER

Highly Effective Ways to Live an Exciting
& Fulfilling Lifestyle

JENNIFER NICOLE LEE

Published by Live Limitless
Authors Academy & Publishing Co.
Publishing@sierrarainge.com

Jennifer Nicole Lee Contact Information :
Website: www.JenniferNicoleLee.com

& Online Coaching Program at www.JNLVIP.com

Printed in the United States of America
Cover Design by: Adam I. Wade
Cover Photo by: Joyanne Panton Photography

ISBN: 978-1-7340469-4-6

Library of Congress Number: 2019915463

MEDICAL DISCLAIMER

The information is this work is in no way intended as medical advice or as a substitute for medical counseling. This publication contains the opinions and ideas of its author.

It is intended to provide helpful and informative material on the subjects addressed in the publication. It is sold with the understanding that the author and publisher are not engaged in rendering medical, health, psychological, or any other kind of personal professional services in the book. If the reader requires personal medical, health, or other assistance or advice, a competent professional should be consulted.

The author and publisher specifically disclaim all responsibility for any liability or loss, personal, or otherwise, that is incurred as a consequence, directly or indirectly of the use and application of the contents of this book. Before starting a weight loss plan, a new eating program, or beginning or modifying an exercise program, check

TABLE OF CONTENT

Dedication

VIP POWER DEDICATION

This book is dedicated to the countless JNL fans and fitness friends around the world. You all simply amaze me! The positive energy you all give to me is a big sign showing that what I do day in and day out really does matter. Furthermore, that my books, programs, and fitness products really have helped you to not only achieve your fitness goals, but to exceed them! Being a Transformational Life Coach, it is my duty to fill the void left wide open by the wellness industry! You see, I created this program out of my very own need and frustrations. I needed a program that that worked effectively and efficiently, that helped me to create and enjoy success in all areas of my life.

I dedicate this VIP book to every woman in the world who works hard, who never gives up, and believes in herself and her fellow VIP sisters! This lifestyle program is for all women, all ages, all shapes, all skin-colors, all sizes, from all over the world! It's a universal program that works! For the busy college student, the real-life working mom, the 9-5'er, the CEO, and the office executive.

Now you hold in your hands, the blueprint for achieving that coveted fitness model physique that you desire! Your emails, phone calls, and letters of love, light, and encouragement telling me how I've helped you achieve your fitness goals are the fuel to my fitness fire. I am successful, because YOU are successful. I know in my mind, body and soul that if I am able to motivate just one person to be better, then I have succeeded in life. To know that I am impacting so many on a global level gives me sheer joy that is priceless. So, I thank you, and I dedicate this book to YOU!

I believe that we all share a common goal; to increase the quality of our lives through living a healthy and fit life. Your desires for a greater well-being have provided me with a continued source of motivation.

May this book awaken the dormant VIP WOMAN in you, and strengthen you mentally, physical, and spiritually. May my fitness expertise, insight, and my motivation help you to achieve your life and your fitness goals; while bringing health, healing, and happiness into your life.

ACKNOWLEDGEMENTS

I want to thank my entire book and publishing team "Live Limitless Author's Academy & Publishing Co." for helping me create and design this book that is a key to unlock the unlimited potential of my fitness friends worldwide.

Also, I'd like to dedicate this book to my foundation; My three kings; my soul-mate husband, Edward, and our two strong and handsome princes, Jaden and Dylan. I would like to also thank my husband for taking my infamous "Before" photo, which helped me to start my weight loss journey. And thank you, Eddie, for loving me then, loving me now and loving me all through my different shapes, weights, and sizes. You have taught me what real, unconditional love is all about.

And to my VIP fitness friends ONLINE at www.JNLVIP.com

I live for training you all online! And I love to be your coach! I love to see you all from every corner of the globe, all online working out! From Australia, Holland, Switzerland, to Canada, all over the UK, to even here in the United States-it's just amazing to see how we all are able to connect online and enjoy a solid "kick butt" JNL VIP workout together! I always take my training sessions seriously, and love to help you get out of your comfort zone, and push our mind, bodies and spirits to the next level.

And thank you to my best friend, Marli, for believing in me. You are my "life coach", always there to listen to me, support me, and help me find my way. Every day you make my life richer, better, and worth living.

You are an angel to me, and I appreciate you! Words cannot express my gratitude for all that you have done to help me and support me!

Remember, keep your VIP power on high, & never bow down to negativity! This empowering book of strength will help you to always keep your head up high, with your invisible VIP cape flowing off of your back! Let's soar to new heights of success!

Smile,
Jennifer Nicole L

Introduction

OPEN LETTER TO VIP WOMEN
ALL OVER THE WORLD

Hello my friends and thank you for taking the time to invest in YOU by purchasing and reading this powerful book! In front of you right now is the master blue print for your VIP success. These words you are about to read will transform your life from "so-so" to "so-so amazing"! If you are sick and tired of being sick and tired, you know you are not living up to your true potential, and you know you can do more, be more, shine more, and have more joy & happiness in all areas of your life, then this book and program is for you!

You don't have to stay stuck! You can RISE UP!

Maybe you have let yourself go. You woke up one day, and felt stuck, you felt uninspired, and like you were going nowhere fast. Maybe you are in a fog, in a funk, and you couldn't see your way out. You feel as if you've lost your way in life, like you've gotten off track, fell off the wagon, and now are searching and yearning for success in your life. When you look at yourself in the mirror, you don't recognize the once youthful woman full of hope. You see a tired, exhausted woman who is drained, lost and confused. Deep down inside you desire change. You wish that you had more energy to get up and go. The job you have may not be fulfilling you. The people at your job are just bringing you down with constant bitterness and negativity. You're exhausted from interactions that don't lift you up, and that drain you.

Maybe every morning when you open your eyes, you just want to go back to sleep because you foresee and expect many problems to come your way in the day. You feel helpless and hopeless. You are afraid of failing again at life, because maybe you have failed before in the past. Maybe you have low self- esteem because you thought you would be further ahead in your life. Maybe it's hard for you to find true joy in your life. You feel stagnant in your success because between work, challenges, unfulfilling relationships, and obstacles in your life, you have been pushed back into a small little scary corner of being comfortably miserable.

The once youthful, vibrant person you were is no longer there. She is replaced with a woman who is jaded and without joy. The woman you once were has become bitter and has lost sight on how to be better. You were once so sweet, but the challenges of life have made you sour. Once better, you are feeling bitter. And once you were joyful, but now you feel jaded..

Well, I've got great news for you! Don't worry because I can and will help you! You see, I once was in these similar situations. I found myself with no drive, no goals and no positive plan of action in my life.

My past is not so pretty. I once weighed over 200 pounds. I had to work at one time 3 dead-end jobs. I had suffered a woman's worst nightmare, a miscarriage, which shattered my personal world, and I felt alone, scared, and full of fear.

I was falling into the trap that my mom fell into, and her mom, and her mom, and so on. You see, my mom was an emotional eater. She ate to console her pain. She over-ate when she really had tough days. She had no schedule, no goals, no plans. And I too picked up these habits of self- destruction. Don't get me wrong. I love my mom, and that's the best she could do at the time. However, these unhealthy habits didn't help me at all, and I too began to live my life that way-lost and confused.

My main objective back then, was every day when I woke up, I just wanted to survive and get through another day. I knew that I was heading for the deep end of failure. Once I fell down, and out, I knew that I might not get up again in life. I was raised on food stamps by a single mother. I wore hand me downs, and ate free government food. I rode the big yellow bus right up until my Senior high school year. I never did fit in. I was always the underdog, and the odd girl out. I was teased, bullied and always made fun of. It caused me deep pain, as a young girl and even contributed to low self –esteem. I didn't believe in myself. I didn't stand for anything, so subsequently, I had a tendency to fall for everything.

Then, one day I became a woman on my own. I still ate food to fill my emotional needs. I would do extreme diets, eating little to nothing and obsessively working out. Needless to say, it wasn't healthy. I had horrible odd jobs, no goals, and no direction in life. My self-care was non-existent, I was failing to take care of myself. I was failing to love myself properly, and quite frankly, it showed.

My personal story gets worse. I had suffered a horrible miscarriage in a 3rd world island with horrible medical care, almost losing my life too. I was visiting Jamaica, with my husband, and we lost our baby. A nightmare that shocked me to truly take care of my health as best as I could! Then I became pregnant with my son Jaden. When Jaden turned 13 months old, I became pregnant with Dylan. For a period of 5 years, I was either pregnant, breastfeeding or just down right out of shape with little to no energy. I was at my all- time low! Plus, I had two little precious babies to take care of. So, I knew something had to change, and change fast! I was frustrated, fed-up, and sick and tired of being sick and tired!

My "A-Ha" Moment"

I remember sitting on the couch with my 2 babies eating pizza and donuts watching TV. I was out of shape, and had little to no energy; It was if God spoke to me and said "You better take drastic action right now, or you will fall into that deep trap of being a nobody, and you won't be able to even take care of your children". It was as if my whole future flashed before my eyes. I was becoming my overweight, and unorganized mom who had no direction or goals in life. In that instance, I jumped off the couch, threw away all the junk food, and made my plan of action.

I decided to wake up early, eat clean, workout, exercise, think positive thoughts, set some huge career goals to and become the woman that I wanted to be-THE VIP WOMAN!

I'm blessed to say that I now run a huge global empire. I am the author of 16 lifestyle books and a Certified Life-Coach. I'm grateful to say that I am living my best life, to my fullest potential. I lost over 80 pounds and I kept it off for close to 17 years. I am so fortunate to have loving and fulfilling relationships. I'm blessed to now enjoy my passion filled and purpose driven VIP life!

When I decided that I deserved a VIP lifestyle, , I chose to take the necessary action steps required to help me transform my life. And I am beyond thrilled to share these success secrets, healthy lifestyle programs, motivational workouts, and life-giving food plans with all of you!

And here is the GREAT NEWS! You too can also transform as well! There is no doubt in my mind whether or not you deserve it. YOU ARE WORTHY OF YOUR BEST LIFE, STARTING RIGHT NOW! It's simple: You must be willing to work for the win that you crave deep within your heart. You can shift the trajectory of your life, you can break bad habits and achieve big goals. You can become a VIP WOMAN!

Who is a VIP Woman?

A VIP Woman has Very Important Person! There are many P's in a VIP Woman's Life that are strong holds of success in her life! They are:

P: Principles-She lives her life guided by the Principles of Success!

P: Plans-She Plans her Work and then Works Her Plan

P: Programs-She has her own personal program of wellness, success, & joy

P: Philosophies-She leans on her wisdom and philosophies in life to create the life of her dreams!

P: Productivity-She is productive! She uses her time wisely! She makes miracles and magic happen daily.

P: Pride-She believes in herself, and she loves the beautiful life she has created for herself and loved ones.

P: and a VIP woman is persistent! She never gives up and always keeps her eye on the PRIZE!

Who is NOT a VIP Woman?

1. A woman who focuses on lack and scarcity

2. A woman who complains instead of finding solutions

3. A woman who has a pity party and feels sorry for herself.

4. A woman who believes she is a victim.

5. A woman who doesn't take control and responsibility in her life.

6. A woman who shrinks and doesn't let her light shine.

7. A woman who stirs the pot, causes drama & gossips

8. A woman who has a low vibrational energy that is always focusing on the negative, not the positive.

9. A woman who is afraid to try and try again.

10. A woman who gives up too easily and is not willing to fight for her rights to a beautiful, balanced and, fulfilling life.

Are you ready to do more, be more, and reclaim your VIP Power?

Then take the following Quizzes below:

#1 VIP QUIZ-QUICKLY ANSWER YES OR NO TO THE FOLLOWING QUESTIONS:

1. Have you gained weight?

2. Do you find yourself often tired or lacking energy?

3. Do you feel stuck?

4. Do you feel like your relationships are draining you?

5. Do you feel like you have settled in your life?

6. When you look into your future, is it bleak?

7. Is your job unfulfilling & draining?

8. Have you lost your purpose in life?

9. Are you frustrated with life, because your needs are being put last?

10. Are you making excuses, sabotaging your very own success?

11. Is the lack of your own self-care negatively affecting other areas of your life?

12. Are you in a relationship with someone who doesn't value you?

13. Do you feel you are being taken advantage of by others?

14. Do you feel like you don't have any voice or say in your life?

15. Do you feel you out of shape?

16. Do you feel like you have aged, and get exhausted easily?

17. Do you feel like you always get the short-end of the stick?

18. Do you go to a job that under pays you and under-values you?

19. Are the people in your life users, always taking from you?

20. Do the people in your life put you down, or don't give you the respect that you feel you deserve?

21. Do you look for external praise or validation from others to know your own personal worth?

If you answered YES to any and all of these questions, then this book & VIP Program will save your life!

This is getting good! Let's continue! Take the second part of this quiz to help you gain more clarity.

#2 VIP QUIZ-QUICKLY ANSWER YES OR NO TO THE FOLLOWING QUESTIONS:

1. Would you like to have more clarity in your life?

2. Would you like to live a more fulfilling life?

3. Do you want a job that is fulfilling & fuels your spirit?

4. Do you want to have an exciting future?

5. Are you ready to find your purpose in life?

6. Do you want to enjoy more freedom in your life?

7. Do you want to create healthy boundaries in your life?

8. Do you desire to have more, be more, earn more?

9. Would you like to lose some weight? To get in shape?

10. Would you like to have endless energy, never getting tired?

11. Are you ready to experience an endless flow of success in your life?

12. Do you want meaningful relationships that fulfill you?

13. Are you ready to grow outside of your comfort zone, and to get to the top, where you belong?

14. Are you ready to create the future of your dreams?

15. Do you desire to have more passion in your profession?

16. Are you ready to find your true passion in life & to live it out daily?

17. Are you ready to put your needs first at the top of your priority list?

18. Are you ready to stop making excuses and to stop sabotaging your very own success?

19. Are you ready to put your self-care, wellness, and fitness rituals first?

20. Are you ready to end all relationships with those who don't value you?

21. Are you ready to use your voice, to let it be heard, and to demand the respect that you deserve?

22. Do you want to age in reverse?

23. Are you ready to get your dream job that pays you what you are worth?

24. Are you ready to increase the value and quality of your social circles?

25. Do you want to network with people who lift you up & give you the respect that you deserve?

26. Are you ready to finally stop seeking validation from other people, and to validate yourself?

Again, if you answered yes to any of the questions above, then you are ready to become a VIP Woman!

Don't be overwhelmed! You can and will achieve your VIP dreams and goals!

I was just like many women out there who find themselves tired, overweight, broke financially and drained physically until I discovered the success secrets to reclaim and unleash my VIP power! You can discover your personal power too!

So, dust off your crown, put it on top of your royal head, and roll out your own red carpet!

Take this 10 Chapter Journey with me, and let's crack your VIP code together. I'm here to help you transform your life and to reclaim & unleash your VIP Power.

Chapter 1

WHO ARE YOU?

"Never forget who you are, for surely the world will not. Make it your strength. Then it can never be your weakness. Armor yourself in it, and it will never be used to hurt you."

~George RR Martin

I can't think of anything more powerful than a woman who is clear about her needs, values, priorities and boundaries. When you know and love who you are, you tend to invest more focus into your personal wellness. Women who practice self-love tend to be more conscious about what they eat, who they interact with, what drains them and what fills them up. They are more likely to surround themselves with what benefits their greater good and their personal interest. Women who have a profound understanding of their worth prioritize their goals. They put themselves first. This is the essence of a VIP woman.

Take this assessment questionnaire below to track your current VIP self-awareness status.

Identity Test & Self-Assessment

In order to reconnect with yourself on a deeper level, and to create the future life of your dreams, you must truly dig deep and become more self-aware.

Take some time to answer each one of these questions, which will then help you to create a VIP Self-Care Program in Chapter Two

1. What are your strengths?

   _____

   _____

   _____

   _____

2. What are your weakness?

   _____

   _____

   _____

   _____

3. When are you at your best?

   _____

   _____

   _____

   _____

4. When are you triggered in a bad way-to do bad?

_____

_____

_____

_____

5. When are you triggered in a good way-to do good?

_____

_____

_____

_____

6. What energizes you?

_____

_____

_____

_____

7. What are you passionate about?

_____

_____

_____

_____

8. What do you love to do the most?

_____

_____

_____

_____

9. What gives you the most joy in life?

_____

_____

_____

_____

10. What are you most passionate about?

_____

_____

_____

_____

11. What fuels you?

_____

_____

_____

_____

12. What fills you up?

_____

_____

_____

_____

13. WHAT DRAINS YOU?

_____

_____

_____

_____

14. When are you at your best?

_____

_____

_____

_____

15. What are you afraid of?

_____

_____

_____

_____

16. Are you daily experiencing inner peace?

_____

_____

_____

_____

17. How much time, money and energy have you invested in your own personal and professional progress?

_____

_____

_____

18. Are your main relationships fulfilling?

_____

_____

_____

_____

19. Do you have a sense of freedom and fulfillment in your relationship?

_____

_____

_____

_____

20. What are your financial goals?

_____

_____

_____

_____

21. What do you value most in life?

_____

_____

_____

_____

22. What are your career goals?

_____

_____

_____

_____

23. What are your wellness goals?

_____
_____
_____
_____

24. What are your fitness and weight loss goals?

_____
_____
_____
_____

25. Where do you want to see yourself in one year from now?

_____
_____

26. In 5 years?

_____
_____

27. In 10 years?

_____
_____

Now that you have taken some time to gain more clarity about where you are and what you truly want and don't want in your life, now you are ready for the next VIP Power step towards your success!

Chapter 2

PUT ON YOUR CROWN & ROLL OUT YOUR OWN RED CARPET

VIPS, you are a star! So, shine up your crowns and roll out your red carpet! Start living your life today like the VIP that you are!

You see, as women, we sometimes wait for validation from others. But in this program, and as your Transformational Coach, I urge you and instruct you to start living your life as the VIP that you are-STARTING TODAY!

How do you do that? Through daily rituals of self-care, self-celebration, goal setting and more!

As a VIP, you need to honor yourself by prioritizing your own self-care.

Self-care is the new health care! It's true! When a woman steps into her VIP Power, she knows first-hand just how important it is to exercise, eat right, get her rest, enjoy her downtime, and not to "run on E" in life. In this chapter, we are going to develop your self-care VIP Program.

As a Master Trainer, I can tell you first-hand how I have witnessed the life changing results of how sticking to an invigorating fitness program, working out, exercising and daily physical activity transforms a woman's life who once had no direction, no self -esteem, with low confidence into a VIP woman with unlimited potential. You see, from motion comes emotion! So, from working out, you will feel strong, empowered, invincible, and worthy. It is so important for you to know that YOU ARE WORTHY of an invigorating workout that will leave you feeling refreshed, rejuvenated and recharged.

As a "Fitness Artist", I know firsthand that there is healing energy through movement! Working out is truly transformational. So, make it a goal to exercise to workout 4-6 times per week for at least 45 minutes to one hour.; And yes, you do have the time! Workout out for one hour is only 4% of your day, that transforms the other 96%. And think about it, someone who is busier than you is working out right now. VIP women make time for the things that serve their greater good. It's your responsibility to make it a (VIP) VERY IMPORTANT PRIORITIY.

Now that I have made it clear just how important working out is, lets continue with the VIP fun!

VIPs in training! Let's find out a little bit more about YOU!

On a scale of 1-10, 1 being the least and 10 being most, please rate the below self-care rituals:

Reading a book

Getting a massage

Enjoying a walk

Meditating

Praying

Journaling

Get a facial

Enjoy some retail therapy

Get a foot massage

Enjoy a hot tea

A day without the kids to unwind

Watching a movie

A power nap

A girl's night out

A day with no schedule

Detoxing hot sauna

Vacation on the beach

Hiking

Charity work

Getting your hair done

Makeup Shopping

Getting a Make Over

Having a Photo Shoot

Getting an extra hour of sleep

Unplugging from all electronics

Being outdoors in nature

Self-care trip, one night to longer

Spending fun time with your pet

Cooking a gourmet meal for yourself

NOTES: Please use this space to fill in any additional notes about your favorite forms of Self-Care:

_____

_____

_____

_____

_____

_____

_____

_____

_____

_____

_____

_____

_____

_____

_____

_____

_____

_____

_____

_____

_____

VIP TIP FOR SUCCESS: Now VIPS, make sure you SCHEDULE IN your self-care rituals and guard that time with everything you have.

We are all different, and so you must know what you really enjoy, so you will feel energized and replenished.

Whatever your self-care program is, USE IT! Remember that you are a VIP Queen, and you deserve daily pampering to keep your cup full and flowing with positivity and productivity.

JOLT OF JNL: When you start to include your daily VIP self-care rituals into your life, you will have a greater sense of self-respect and a better sense of importance. This energy will flow into all areas of your life. Others in your immediate social, personal and professional circle will see this and also take notice. So, keep at it VIP.

FITNESS, WORKING OUT, & EXERCISING-WHY IT'S AN IMPORTANT FOUNDATION TO BUILD YOUR VIP POWER UPON.

Working out is a corner stone of success and It's the epitome of self-care.

Why be the richest woman in the graveyard; buried 6 feet under, because you lived an unbalanced life where you focused more on your career and neglected your health. Why be a broke fitness enthusiast, where all you focus on is your physique, and then let your career and finances dwindle. I'm here to help you create a healthy balance between work and self-care.

Let's get real: working out and exercising are not just healthy for you, but it improves all areas of your life. It empowers you and give you that glow, energy, stamina, mental focus and endurance you need to push through in all other areas in your life.

VIP FACT: How to never miss a workout: Put it into your weekly planner! Make sure you schedule your workouts into your calendar, as if they were important business meetings that you cannot cancel out on, call in sick to, or fail to show up to. After all, this meeting is with the most important person in the world-YOU.

QUESTION FOR JNL: Jennifer, I work two jobs and I'm a single parent, also raising my children. Time and budget are what hold me back. I feel like I don't have time to get to the gym and workout, plus its expensive! HELP!

ANSWER: VIP woman, I feel you! This is why I created the online coaching program

If you feel like you have let yourself go, and you need to lose fat & gain lean muscle tone, but don't have a lot of time and are on a strict financial budget, then you should join my www.JNLVIP.com program where you will get live-stream workouts every week, access to over hundreds of exercise workout videos on demand, group coaching on nutrition, fat loss supplements, plus so much more.

Chapter 3

WHO ARE YOU ROLLING WITH?

The saying is true "You become the 5 people you surround yourself with". The simple truth is that you are the average of the five people you spend the most time with. If you show me your friends, I will show you your future. We've all heard these phrases before and we know just how true they are. Plain and simple, your circle will either influence you to grow, or box you in with limited perspective and resources.

Every VIP woman has a VIP Squad. Surround yourself with people who push you to do and be better. No drama or negativity. Just higher goals and higher motivation. Good times and positive energy only. No jealously or hate. Simply bringing out the absolute best in each other.

VIP SOCIAL CIRCLE QUIZ: ANSWER YES OR NO TO THE QUESTIONS BELOW:

Are the top 5 people in your life:

1. Do they drain you?

2. Do they hold you back?

3. Do they get on your nerves?

4. Do they treat you bad?

5. Do they take you for granted?

6. Do they try to undermine you?

7. Do they disrespect you?

8. Do they give you bad vibes?

9. Do they disregard your needs and wants?

10. Do they make you feel bad about yourself?

11. Do they make you feel that no matter what you do, it's not good enough?

12. Do they turn a blind eye when something good happens to you?

VIP SOCIAL CIRCLE QUIZ: ANSWER YES OR NO TO THE QUESTIONS BELOW:

Would you like to have people in your life that:

1. Root for you to rise?

2. Cheer you on to new levels of success?

3. Help you achieve your goals?

4. Put your goals as a top priority?

5. Who are genuinely happy for you when you succeed?

6. Who are there to help you achieve new heights of success?

7. Help open new doors for you?

8. Fuel your energy?

9. Make you feel happy, joyful, loved and appreciated?

10. Are loyal, nonjudgmental, and honest?

11. You are proud of? And you want to introduce to your other VIP friends?

LET'S DIG DEEPER:

LIST BELOW THE TOP 5 PEOPLE YOU HANG OUT WITH, AND WHY-

1.

2.

3.

4.

5.

What are the 5 things you love about them?

_____

_____

_____

_____

_____

What do they do?

_____

_____

_____

_____

_____

_____

_____

_____

_____

_____

Do you complement one another?

Are these relationships a Win-Win, where you both benefit?

What are the benefits of the connection?

Do you reciprocate what they give to you?

Do they help you level up in life?

VIP Success Tip: When You take more than you give in any relationship, you become a liability, not an asset, and you become easily replaceable!

The Importance of Community & Camaraderie

QUESITONS FOR JNL: Jennifer, I love my husband and kids. However, they are busy. It's not that they don't love me or care about my goals, it's just that my children are in school, and have their extracurricular activities; And my husband loves me, but he travels a lot and has his personal hobbies that really don't interest me. Sometimes I need healthy, positive reinforcement or nurturing relationships to lean on. HELP!

ANSWER: Great question! The importance of community is essential to a VIP's lifelong success. A VIP woman knows that she can get support, help, guidance and invaluable friendship from other like-minded women. This is why I created a community of VIP women who share common goals of wanting to achieve and enjoy success in all areas of their lives. Please visit www.JNLVIP.com for more info and join today for only $1 for your first 30 days. The online fitness friendships and support you get will help to fill in the void that a modern-day woman needs in order to live a full and robust life!

VIP DECLARATRION-BILL OF RIGHTS!

VIP's Knowing your Rights is essential to living your best life to its fullest capacity!

Daily affirm your VIP Power by reading out loud your VIP Declaration and Bill of Rights

I WILL RECLAIM & UNLEASH
MY VIP POWER!

I WILL LIVE MY LIFE
AT MY FULLEST CAPACITY!

I HONOR RELATIONSHIPS
THAT HONOR ME!

I WILL ENJOY DAILY SELF-CARE
RITUALS THAT KEEP MY CUP FULL!

I WILL ONLY SERVE OTHERS FROM MY
OVERFLOW, BECAUSE MY FULL CUP IS
FOR ME!

I WILL SET NEW GOALS FOR MYSELF
AND CRUSH THEM!

I AM AND ALWAYS WILL BE ENOUGH!

I AM COURAGEOUS AND WILL STAND UP
FOR MY VIP POWER!

I AM A POWERFUL CREATOR!

I TRUST MY INTUITION AND ALWAYS
MAKE WISE DECISIONS!

I CREATE THE LIFE I WANT
AND I ENJOY IT!

I AM SURROUNDED BY SUPPORTIVE
POSITIVE PEOPLE WHO BELIEVE IN ME
AND WANT TO SEE ME SUCCEED!

I HAVE THE VIP POWER TO CREATE
POSITIVE CHANGE IN MY LIFE!

FEELING CONFIDENT, ASSURED, AND
STRONG IS A NORMAL PART OF MY
EVERY DAY LIFE!

Chapter 4

VIP PROGRAMMING & PROGRAMS

"I was once afraid of people saying, "Who does she think she is?" Now I have the courage to stand and say, "This is who I am."

-Oprah Winfrey

It's plain and simple. Very Important People have "Very Important Programing" and "Very Important Programs" that they stick to.

It's true, before I became successful, focused and disciplined with my goals of winning in all areas of my life, my "program" for life was just to get by. My mindset was limited to that of merely surviving. I often just went with the flow, accepting whatever life handed me.

As I started my personal self -help journey, I soon realized that I too had to "Re-Program" myself. I had to replace my old, archaic, out dated habits with new ones that actually served me.

So instead of:

1. Sleeping in-I woke up early every day at the same time.

2. Going to be late-I went to bed early every day at the same time.

3. Worrying-I become a warrior.

4. Going with the flow-I started to create and design the life that I wanted to live.

5. Instead of crying victim-I started to choose to be victorious.

6. Focusing on the problem-I started to create solutions to my problems.

7. Instead of trying to fix everyone's problems-I let go and let God, instead of me trying to be God and fix everyone's problems, which was draining

8. I swapped out looking frazzled and flustered-And made sure that I was put together, polished and poised!

You see, just like a computer, we are all wired or programed a certain way, either for success or to be unsuccessful. To be fearful, or to be full of faith. To be full of confusion, or have clarity. So, in this chapter, we are going to address how to RE-PROGRAM ourselves for unlimited success.

Let's dig deeper.

We all function from our subconscious mind. We have 80,000-90,000 thoughts per day, and all of them are subconscious! So, no wonder we sometimes self-sabotage our success.

So, we must look deep at our belief systems to see what is hurting us or helping us.

MEET DEBORAH & LISTEN TO HER STORY:

Meet Deborah, a cheery, positive fun-loving fitness enthusiast who never missed a workout and was on the highway to success. She was one of my clients, and she had a shift in her life, which caused her to temporarily move in with her mother and her mother's new husband. The tension that she felt between her mom and her step dad caused her a great deal of stress. Deborah began to feel down, depressed, and even started to experience mood swings. She felt the negativity and how it affected her mom. Due to her proximity to negative interactions, she started to absorb a lot of that bad juju. She then stopped working out. She started to overeat to soothe her diminished emotional state. She even started to drink to calm her nerves and escape the bad emotions that she was feeling. Needless to say, the temporary move in with her mom caused her years of stress and it derailed her success. It hit her like a ton of bricks. She was exposed to negative energy and it directly affected every aspect of her life. I told her to move out immediately, and to also tell her mom to take care of herself. She moved out, and got back on her program and back on her fast-track to success.

MEET JULIE & LISTEN TO HER STORY:

Julie was always a ray of sunshine. When her grandmother got sick, she would visit her daily to provide care for her. She started to notice that she was feeling down and she started to get depressed, worried and full of anxiety. It was enough that her grandmother was sick, but then her grandmother would always play the news and watch drama filled soap operas as her pastime. Just being in her grandmother's house made her feel anxious and on edge. She was subconsciously absorbing all of the negative energy from the news, and the drama from the soap operas. She was actually quite aware of why she started to have a decline in positive energy. She decided to speak with her grandmother about it. Julie then exchanged the depressing news and soap opera drama for uplifting positive YouTube videos. She would play affirming videos with positive messages for her grandmother. Together they would say positive affirmations from a guided meditation video that they found online. They would sing uplifting songs and rejoice in delight and gratitude for life, health and strength. In no time, Julie started to feel better, and so did her Grandmother! You see, what you digest, and what you put into your mind, body and spirit will affect the outcome of your life. This includes food, media, videos, music, and even the things you tell yourself. Whether it's the negative self -talk or the positive affirmations that you recite, your life will be a reflection of the programming you take in.

Are you ready for ULTIMATE SUCCESS?

You have to stop believing in limited thoughts in order to crush your Limiting Belief System!

VIP Success Tip: Your mind, belief systems and your subconscious thoughts can either help you or hinder you on your success journey. Thoughts are so powerful! Thoughts become things. Thoughts are words that you just don't verbally say. So be mindful of your mind, beliefs, and thoughts, and make them powerful and positive!

SEEK and YE SHALL FIND!

If you are looking for pain in your life, you will find it.

If you are looking for happiness in your life, you will find it.

It's a powerful Universal rule! Whatever you are seeking, is also then silently seeking you!

When you are REPROGRAMING yourself and creating your new VIP Program on how you want to live your life, make it a practice to wake up expecting success, seeking happiness, requesting abundance, joy, health and love in your life-and believe that it will show up!

DAILY PRACTICE:

If you are going to have lasting results, you have to engage in daily rituals. You wouldn't take one shower and assume that you will be clean for the rest of your life. You don't go to the gym once and expect to be in shape for the rest of your life. You don't go to church once to have an amazing relationship with your higher power for the rest of your life. Get the point? You need to have DAILY rituals, habits, and program regimens in order to have LONG TERM SUCCESS!

For example: how many of you learned a foreign language in college, and today you can't even say a few sentences! So, you have to learn and grow through continued utility and practice. This is where events come into play! In order to use all of your VIP POWER, you have to get to an event, a wellness retreat, a fitness weekend, a seminar, an online webinar to USE what you have learned. Immerse yourself in continued learning so that you don't lose what you've learned. Make sure you seek out the next VIP Seminar in your area, or online. You can even get daily motivation at our online coaching program at www.JNLVIP.com So in closing, in order to keep and grow your VIP power, you must use it daily. And a community, live online and in person events, coaching, working out, group activities with a like-minded community are what strengthen your VIP power.

CHANGE YOUR EXPECTATIONS FOR APPRECIATION

Sadly enough, when you don't have your expectations met when you have been working so hard it can impact your self-esteem. When you get little to no results after putting forth tons of effort, it's easy to get bummed and to feel down and even angry. It's more effective when you replace your expectations with appreciation and gratitude.

TRAIN YOUR BRAIN

Use your brain, or it will start using YOU! Have you ever felt so stretched thin that your brain was just run ragged? Well, you have got to gain control over your mind so that you are a master over it and it has less control over you.

Be your own best friend instead of your own worst enemy. It all starts with your mindset, and how you train your thoughts to serve your greater good! VIP Tip: Flip it! When a negative thought comes in, immediately flip it to the exact opposite. It's a fun mental trick that works! For example, when you say to yourself "I will never get in shape!" flip it immediately to "I'm in great shape, and I will continue to work on my fitness goals daily to get to my goals, and it will be FUN!" Your mind goes into positive mode, believing the uplifting message you just told yourself, and it energizes you to continue on your wellness journey.

LET GO OF OLD PROGRAMS, & REPLACE NEW ONES

When you talk about-it's a dream.

When you visualize it-it's cool & exciting.

When you schedule it-it becomes real! So commit to it! Put it on your calendar! Put it on your planner! When you take it from your mind and write it down on paper, it becomes a physical manifestation and you are one step closer to your goal.

GO FROM PEAK TO PEAK

Plan your goals in advance. When you crush a goal you feel great! Most of us don't celebrate our wins long enough. Once we achieve one goal, we tend to move on quickly to the next vision. The problem with this, is that, after you experience a win, your high of winning is short lived and you experience a low. There's this up and down sensation that causes you to experience a roller coaster of emotions.

If you keep planning your big power moves, your goals, and you keep them packed on your calendar, you will be effectively reprograming yourself to become the VIP WOMAN that you want to be! The key is to set goals, but to celebrate every win along the way no matter how big or small.

Don't let opportunity escape your grasp.

IF YOU WANT TO CHANGE THE WORLD, AND CHANGE OTHER PEOPLE, YOU HAVE TO FIRST START WITH CHANGING YOURSELF.

Let's get real: We really don't have the power to change anyone. The power to change is an inside job. You can change yourself and allow others to be inspired by your transformation so much so that they choose to take action in their own lives. You have to become the change that you want to see in the world. You must be an example of the change that you desire to see in others. Once you become what you aspire to be, you will then attract others like you. Not only do you raise the bar, but your inspired action continues to raise the bar to new heights.

YOU ARE WHAT YOU CONSUME, WHETHER IT IS FOOD AND ALSO MEDIA! We all agree that thoughts become things. Well, what about the media that you watch and or listen to? Like The music, social media, TV, radio, news you (either consciously or subconsciously) absorb daily has a direct impact on your overall wellness. The media you consume daily eventually will manifest in your reality. So please make sure are "consuming" positive media that will help you become the VIP woman that you want to be. Your social media, videos, music, books and movies you enjoy should lift you up in your mood, spirit, and give you food feelings of positivity.

Stay away from negative news, soap operas, and reality T.V shows that evoke jealously and other bad emotions. These forms of media will cause negativity in your mind, body, and spirit.

Instead, replace negative media with positive videos, audio books, guided meditations, positive affirmations, music and movies.

Feed your mind positive media every day! Rewire it, retrain it to see the good, expect the good, and believe that you can create your dream VIP life.

YOUR LIFE IS THE RESULT OF YOUR INPUT

Keep the momentum going by making sure that you engage in daily rituals of positive affirmations, guided meditations, praying, journal writing, and listening to positive audio books, seminars, and or group coaching calls. I offer tons of supportive media in my Private coaching group that you can listen to while you are getting dressed in the morning, running errands, or commuting to work.

DON'T ENTERATIN NEGATIVE PEOPLE! IT'S A TRAP!

Do you know someone who always like to "stir-the-pot" causing negative energy? Stay away from them! It's a trap. I call them energy vampires. Delete them from your phone, and block them on social media. It's time for you to clean house by ridding your space of non-VIP like women. This allows you to make room for women who are supportive, kind and uplifting. It's plain and simple. VIP Women know their value. They understand their worth. They only entertain other like-minded-women, never "bowing down" to women who are only out to under-mine or sabotage their success.

END ALL NEGATIVE SELF TALK

I had to finally put an end to my negative self- talk. Growing up being teased, bullied, and never quite fitting in, I suffered from my own negative narratives. I was raised on food stamps, I wore hand-me-downs, and I ate free lunch at school. I honestly never felt like I was good enough. These early feelings of despair, lack, and not being "good enough" stayed with me for a long time. I had to TRAIN MYSELF to stop feeling bad about myself.

THE VIP POSITIVE TALK METHOD

How did I do this? I used what I call now the "VIP Positive Talk Method". As soon as a negative thought would pop into my mind, I would recognize it, and then completely flip it to be the exact opposite.

Read examples below in which you too can shift your negative dialogue! Get ready because they are powerful!

1. I'm fat VS. I'm so curvy, healthy and voluptuous! I love my healthy curvy body! I'm getting in better shape every day!

2. This outfit looks stupid VS. I'm rocking this unique look, and I'm so confident that I don't want to fit in, because I love to stand out. I am OUT-STANDING!

3. I am not qualified for this position VS I am so excited to learn. I am highly coachable, and I will do all that I can do, and be willing to learn what I don't know.   I am a team player.

4. I'm not happy with my life VS I may not be where I want to be in life, but I'm excited to be on the right path. I'm designing my dream life. God is on my side and the entire Universe is conspiring for me to win!

5. I don't want to do this today VS I may not be so excited about this right now, but I am excited to learn a new skill, meet new people, and showcase just what an amazing person I am! Let my VIP LIGHT SHINE! I'm grateful for another day, another opportunity and I believe in miracles. I know a miracle will come out of this!

VIP REPROGRAMING REQUIRES "PRIMING"

CALL TO ACTION: Take a listen to this powerful MORNING MINDFULNESS MEDITATION

Create a subconscious anticipation of JOY, HAPPINESS, AND OF FEELING SO BLESSED!

Improve your mental and emotional state by starting your day off right!

Listen, it's so true:

When you WIN THE MORNING, You WIN THE DAY! And when you WIN THE DAY, You WIN THE WEEK! When you WIN THE WEEK, You WIN THE MONTH! When you WIN THE MONTH, You WIN THE YEAR! And when you WIN THE YEARS, YOU experience a winning LIFE!

Start by winning the MORNING!

How? By starting your day with

1. Prayer

2. Gratitude

3. Positive Video of a Morning Mindfulness Meditation

What does this do? These VIP Morning Priming Rituals will help you WIN THE MORNING! It will put you into a STATE of VIP POWER and allow you to gain an overall sense of WINNING!

It's a daily discipline and you should never have an excuse to not do it!

It takes 10-15 minutes, so you can do it every day. No excuses!

VIP VIDEO LIBRARY FOR ULTIMATE SUCCESS-LISTEN & WATCH THOSE EXCLUSIVE VIDEOS TO PROGRAM YOURSELF FOR SUCCESS

VIPS!

I took the time to film and record some REPROGRAMMING videos just for you!

Please visit www.VIPMeditation.com for your Morning Motivation Meditation

Visit www.VIPAbundance.com for how to increase financial prosperity in your life.

Go to www.VIPProductivity.com to prime yourself to be more productive in your life.

Visit www.VIPPositivity.com to listen to a guided meditation to increase positivity in all areas of your life.

VIP MORNING PROGRAM

Remember that important quote;

WIN THE MORNING, WIN THE DAY. WIN THE DAY, WIN THE WEEK. WIN THE WEEK, WIN THE MONTH. WIN THE MONTH, WIN THE YEARS. WIN THE YEARS, WIN AT LIFE!

Well, how do you win the morning? Every morning? As I mentioned before, you prime yourself with prayer, gratitude and positive media to kick-start your day.

Let's take it one step further and cover physical fitness and food in the next chapters. This is where the real VIP Magic and success breakthroughs begin!

Chapter 5

VIP PHYSICAL FITNESS

It's not exercise. It's an EXPERIENCE! One that transforms a normal day, into an EXTRA-ORDINARY DAY! VIP PHYSCIAL FITNESS

As I mentioned earlier on in Chapter 2, I made the point of why working out is an important foundation to building your VIP power. It's truly a corner stone of success, and the epitome of self-care.

In this chapter, I am going to explain the top reasons why it's essential to workout 4-6 times per week consistently. We will also discuss how to make sure you always get your workouts in.

As you all may know by now, fitness changed my life from being "so-so" to "so-so" strong and successful. !"

It transformed me from being sick and tired to being full of positive energy. Fitness allowed me to develop an "I Can Do It" attitude. Working out transformed my self-doubt into an unbreakable confidence!

It helped me to become grateful, instead of grumpy. It's extremely empowering to work out and get all pumped up. It helps you to feel and look amazing!

This is Your Brain on Exercise:

It's not only your muscles that get stronger when you exercise; your brain gets stronger too.

Exercising protects your brain from depression, Alzheimer's disease, and even dementia.

The benefits of physical fitness are long lasting!

Here is a list of advantages that your brain enjoys from exercising!

These benefits are better than a cup of coffee! So, put down the caffeine and pick up the cardio and strength training.

1. Improved mood.

2. Improved Cognitive health.

3. Improved Brain Health.

4. Triggers growth of new blood vessels in the brain.

5. Boosts "better fed & healthier" brain cells.

6. Boosts Creativity.

7. Increased memory.

8. Increased Focus.

9. Increased Ability to maintain attention on tasks.

10. Your brain can multitask better, focusing on multiple projects at once.

WHO WANTS TO GET HIGH?

Did you know that you can enjoy a natural high with no crashing, no relapsing and you don't need to see your corner neighborhood drug dealer to get it. You can't even buy it or get a prescription for it.

You see, your brain creates it when you work out.

It's called Dopamine.

DO IT AND DO IT OFTEN!

Listen up VIPs in training: Your conscious brain might loathe working out, but your body secretly craves it. The brain is on your side when you want to make working out a daily habit. How? Well, it releases good feeling chemicals when you are doing it.

VIP WORKOUT TRICK:

"JNL, I never feel like working out, even though I know deep down inside that I must workout in order to reach my fat loss goals. HELP! Great point. Here is your solution. You see, you may not be naturally motivated. And in all actuality, from movement and getting moving, you create motivation. I understand from the start that you must get moving first, and then the motivation will start to kick in 5-8 minutes into your workout, because you start to stimulate your dopamine, a neurotransmitter that is responsible for transmitting signals in between the newer cells of the brain, kick in in that "feel-good" energy. So, trick your body by setting a timer for 5 minutes, and start moving! Once you start, you can't stop! And I can assure you that an entire hour-long workout will fly by!

Dopamine

This is a chemical in your brain that is a neurotransmitter. It's your own personal "coach" inside of your brain that inspires you to crush your goals. And get this, not only does it motivate you, but it gives you a rush of pleasure after you take positive action toward your desires.

BUT WAIT, THERES MORE!

In addition to Dopamine, there are three more hormones that you can trigger to make you feel better. They are serotonin, oxytocin, and endorphins.

When you feel special or important, serotonin will be released. It's true that during and after a workout, you feel accomplished, special and important. This is why working out is nothing short of a miracle.

Oxytocin is the "hug hormone" and is released during physical contact. I suggest enjoying 5-8 hugs a day. I am a hugger. I love to give hugs and receive them! They promote healing and they do wonders for boosting your mood. Don't have anyone to hug? No problem; Hug yourself!

Endorphins are released as a response to stress or pain. Have you ever gotten that second wind during a workout? Or ten minutes into your workout, you feel that natural high kick in? Have you ever felt like at the beginning of your workout you didn't want to train, but 10 minutes into it, you can't stop? This is the result of your endorphins being released and your dopamine being stimulated and positively triggered.

PHYISCAL FITNESS CREATES VITAMIN C!

Take your Vitamin C daily! No, not the kind that you get from an orange. The kind that is created from working out! I'm talking about the Vitamin C for CONFIDENCE!

Don't you feel fabulous after a workout? Like you are invincible? A super hero? With an invisible cape flowing off of your back? This is the confidence that you create from working out. It's a VIP Power that you must tap into.

FROM MOTION COMES EMOTION!

Most people are not happy simply because they don't move. We live in a world of convenience. We have been so trained to not walk, move about or be active. For instance, we will circle the parking lot looking for a close parking space, instead of just simply parking further away and enjoying a brisk walk.

Here's the thing, the more you move, the more you FEEL FANTASTIC!

If you ever feel stuck, just MOVE! Movement also opens up your creative energy, boosting your brains focus.

VIP TIP: "JNL, I'm very short on time, as I have many demands and responsibilities on me that I must take care of. Any solutions for helping me never to miss a workout, and to at least boost my energy for the day?" You are not alone! Keep reading and when you are short on time, do this VIP Circuit to boost your mood, energy, fat loss results and confidence! I like to call this a "Fitness Snack" as one of my VIP clients once called it! Perform 30 seconds of each move below. While you are moving, repeat your favorite positive affirmations. When you are in a peak state of working out and moving, whatever you hear and or tell yourself will become branded into your subconscious. So, go for it!

1. Jumping Jacks
2. Burpees

3. Push-ups (on your knees if you need to).

4. Air Jump Rope

5. Ab crunches

6. Plank

End this mini-routine with 4 deep inhales. This will energize you, and help you feel fabulous!

VIP PROGRAMS to MAKE SURE YOU NEVER MISS A WORKOUT

Have the intention of working out 4-6 times per week? But for some reason it never happens? Or you work out consistently for 2 weeks, and then you stop?

Here are some VIP Programing Hacks you can do daily to ensure workout success!

1. Circle the days on your monthly or weekly calendar that you have committed to working out.

2. Lay out your workout clothes the night before.

3. Have your post workout meal prepared or even just decide on what it is going to be.

4. Decide to work out the same time every day. This habit of knowing when you are going to work out during the day will allow you to build the rest of your schedule around it.

5. Aim to workout first thing in the morning. Why? So that you can begin your workout before your brain catches on and tries to stop you! Also, you burn fat all day long, thus setting yourself up for long term fat loss & fitness success.

As you can see, working out and implementing physical fitness is so much more than just looking good in a bikini! It's essential for optimal brain health, energy, focus, stamina, and confidence!

So VIPS, get your sweat on!

Chapter 6

FOOD-FUEL UP LIKE A VIP

You can't function off of the "Cigarette and Red Bull Diet" trap that I see many entrepreneurs falling into. Long days, late nights, and Uber Eats on speed dial will burn you out fast. You will only "crash and burn", and also gain tons of weight. So, in this Chapter, we are going to talk about the importance of a healthy, balanced, highly nutritious food plan, so you can FUEL UP like a VIP!

And this is truly my favorite chapter—the chapter on food! Repeat after me: "I love food, and food loves me." It's time we start enjoying a healthy relationship with food! That's the great part about the VIP diet; it isn't really a diet! We're going to plan our food, so let's call it a food plan, rather than dieting. Because look at the word DIE-T! The first 3 letters are DIE! Who wants that?

This is where you're going to stop eating accidentally and start eating optimally. You're going to enjoy eating anti-aging super foods that will help you to look and feel your best! You're also going to detoxify through eating the right foods.

Optimal Nutrition

Since VIPS deserve the best I must make sure that our nutrition is spot on. Crash or fat diets are not allowed. For close to two decades, I have been a specialist in Sports Nutrition & Supplementation, and I have seen it first hand in my life, and in my clients lives just how important optimal nutrition is.

What is Optimal Nutrition? It is eating and supplementing for optimal performance. Instead of focusing on fad diets, we focus on super foods, and nutritionally dense foods, so that you are enjoying a food plan that is antioxidant rich and moderate in lean sources of protein and slow burning complex carbs. This will help you to build and maintain sexy, sleek muscle tone to keep your energy on high so that you can slay the day away!

You are What You Eat!

This old adage is absolutely true! If you eat a fat-burger and a side of greasy fries, you will feel sluggish, bloated, and weighed down. But If you eat a high-vibrational power smoothie, you will feel energetic and recharged.

VIP Food Plan Tip: Plan your food in advance. And always ask yourself "How will I feel after I eat this?" If your mind tells you bad, then don't eat it, no matter how much you crave it! If your mind says "fabulous, upbeat, well-nourished" then GO FOR IT!

It's Not Only What You Eat, But WHEN YOU EAT

VIPs know the importance of spacing out your calories throughout the day in order to keep your engine humming all day long. They also know that they need to fuel the start of their day right. They focus on burning fat instead of storing it.

How a Farmer Fattens a Pig

True story! I'm from Tennessee and I've seen it first-hand. A farmer fattens their pigs by "starving" them for at least 24 hours. This ensures that they are really hungry. Then they unleash endless amounts of food until they can't eat anymore, letting them gorge and binge. This method of feeding the pigs does many things in order to fatten the them up. First, when a pig hasn't eaten in a while, their metabolism shuts down, thus any calories they eat will be stored and not burned off. Second, when a pig hasn't eaten in a while, or is not on a steady feeding schedule, they will eat as much as they can out of the fear that they won't be eating again any time soon. Does this sound familiar? Maybe you have been eating in a somewhat similar cycle, where you didn't eat breakfast because you weren't hungry, or you were trying to "save" calories; and then you skipped lunch because you had tons of work to do. Maybe you couldn't break away from your work and then you found yourself completely starving by dinner time that you ate everything in sight! You binge and after your feast, you feel so completely exhausted that you go to bed in a food coma that you have to just "sleep off". Then, you wake up with a "food hangover", still full from the night before, that you skip breakfast, bypass eating lunch again, and then binge at dinner. You are eating just like the pig being fatted on the farm! Don't do this to yourself! Instead, eat a healthy breakfast, lunch, and dinner. Be sure to add a snack in between meals if you feel hungry. A VIP Rule is to eat every 2-3 hours to keep your energy flowing, your blood sugar stable, and your metabolism revved up.

Don't live to eat! Instead eat to LIVE!

Food is fuel. Think of it this way. The better the fuel, the better you function. Eating food with a focus to perform better, build stronger muscles, have more energy, more brain power and to have more endurance is the way to go. If you are not eating enough healthy, slow-burning carbs, such as brown rice, sweet potatoes, or oatmeal, you will crash and burn. If you are not eating enough healthy fats such as avocados and nuts, you will have a decrease in brain function and focus. If you don't get enough protein, you won't have the necessary building blocks to grow, repair and build sexy lean muscle tone.

These 3 main components of food are called MACROS

VIPS KNOWS THEIR MACROS

It's important to know your macros and what they do. Macros means "large". So, your body needs large amounts of these macros in order to function properly

1. Carbs are used as fuel and energy. Eat complex carbs, not simple carbs. Stay away from sugar, candy, and white starches. Opt for complex carbs, which are fiber rich, with vitamins and minerals.

2. Proteins are used for preserving lean muscle mass. Protein is found in animal and plant based protein.

3. Fat is needed for growth, development and energy. Fat acts like a cushioning agent to protect your organs. It's found in oils, fish, meat, and some grains. Stay away from trans fats, which are formed through hydrogenated oils. Trans fats lead to heart disease and are found in baked goods, preserved foods, doughs, and margarines.

HOW MANY MACROS DO I NEED?

Well, that depends! I can't really say as it varies from person to person, depending upon how physically active they are. Basic guidelines are 45-65% Carbs, 10-35%

Protein, & 20-35% fats. These numbers are debatable, but at least this gives you a starting guide.

VIP FUEL UP FOOD GUIDE GOLDEN RULES:

1. Eat whole foods
2. Eat High-Vibrational Foods-such as nuts, seeds, deeply colored fruits and vegetables, dark leafy greens.
3. If man made it, don't eat it
4. Stay away from Fast Food
5. Aim to Meal Prep
6. Drink lots of water
7. Reduce your Alcohol intake. Better yet, don't drink at all.
8. Drink more Smoothies.
9. Eat every 2-3 hours.
10. Supplement like an athlete.

Quick snack options on the go

1. Handful of nuts with an apple
2. Rice cake topped with peanut butter and sugar free preserves
3. Hummus and carrots
4. Low fat string cheese and a small piece of fruit.

5. Banana with low-fat peanut putter drizzled with sugar free syrup.

6. Small can of tuna fish, with a side of whole grain crackers.

7. Whole grain tortilla wrapped with grilled lean chicken strips, with tomato and lettuce.

8. Vegetable and fruit Smoothie.

9. Protein Shake made with water.

10. Low Carb Protein Bar.

MICRONUTRIENTS

Okay VIPS, we now know our Macronutrients. Let's briefly cover Micronutrients. Micro means small, therefore we need these in small amounts.

MICROS are vitamins, minerals, antioxidants, and phytochemicals.

Benefits of Micros are:

1. They keep your immune system strong

2. They support Bone health

3. To support all functions of the body

4. They keep your body running optimally

5. They help in the production of enzymes

6. They help in the production of hormones

7. They help in the production of proteins that are critical to the body

8. They support brain function

9. They help the regulation of metabolism

10. They help in regulating your heartbeat.

With a busy VIP lifestyle, it's sometimes hard to get all of your micronutrients in. This is why I highly suggest you supplement.

VIP Essential Supplements:

When you start running your life like a VIP, you've got to supplement like one. You can't be pounding down Starbucks every day to give you energy. You will only crash and burn. Caffeine is what I call "fake" energy. You must get all of your vitamins and minerals in order to have real energy that supports your immune system and fight off disease. One way to do this is to take a good multivitamin. When selecting a multivitamin, make sure it's a highly reputable brand.

BCAAS

BCAAS is short for Branch Chain Amino Acids. They build muscle and help you maintain your muscle mass. They are essential amino acids, which comprise about 35% of your muscles protein.

Your body doesn't make them, so it's essential to get them either from food or from supplements. They are the building blocks of protein.

BCAAS help you to restore and maintain your glycogen stores, which is important because they lessen protein break down during exercise. It has been said that when you take BCAAS you have more energy and stamina in your workouts. Therefore you can train longer to get more results.

JNL, how can I get my BCAAS?

Great question! I suggest that you drink them before, during and after your workout. There are many different BCAA workout drinks, powders, and capsules on the market that you can enjoy. Just make sure you look for those that have 5 grams of leucine, 4 grams of valine and 2 grams of isoleucine for maximum support.

Concise List of Benefits from BCAAS:

1. Reduces your fatigue from exercising

2. Reduces muscle soreness post workout

3. Helps to maintain your lean muscle mass

VIP Meal Plan Program

VIPs, let me make this so simple for you! Here are some guidelines to use when creating your meals and knowing what to eat.

65

VIP Meal Composition:

When creating your meals, make sure you have a lean source of protein, with a slow burning complex carb, a fibrous carb, and some healthy fat.

Below are lists of each meal component:

20 GRAMS/3-4 OUNCES LEAN SOURCE OF PROTIEN

Eggs

Turkey

Fish

Chicken

Plain Greek Yogurt

Beans, Peas, Lentils

Low fat cottage cheese

Lite Tofu

Tempeh

Lean beef

Pork Loin

Shrimp

½ CUP SLOW BURNING COMPLEX CARBS

Brown rice

Sweet Potatoes

Whole grain pasta

Whole grain bread

Oatmeal

Whole Grain Tortilla

Quinoa

Buckwheat

Beans

½ CUP OF FIBROUS CARBS

Broccoli

Brussel sprouts

Cabbage

Carrots

Cauliflower

Celery

Cucumber

Lettuce

Spinach

Mushrooms

Zucchini

Watermelon

Apples

Oranges

Grapes

Pretty much all vegetables & fruits.

1 TEASPOON HEALTHY FATS

Avocado

Nuts

Seeds

Coconut oil

Olive Oil

Chia seeds

JNL, WHEN SHOULD I EAT CARBS?

Great question! Make sure you focus on your complex carb intake early on in the day. Eat a complex carb with your breakfast, post-workout, and during lunch. A general rule of thumb is to not have any complex carbs after 4:00pm. So, for dinner, you would have a lean source of protein, with a fibrous carb, which are vegetables. So, skip the breadbasket, and say no to the pasta. Say yes to a side of steamed vegetables or a small green salad. Why? Because the complex carbs you eat at night will be stored in your body, and not burned off as fuel. Plus, you need the energy during the day to take care of your VIP business.

For more information, support and to download a 14 Day VIP Food Plan with Recipes & BONUS Juicing Recipe Section make sure you visit (bit.ly/JNLVIPMEALS)

Hello VIP! Welcome to the VIP 14 Day Super Food Fat Loss Meal Plan. This section is complete with recipes and a Bonus Juicing recipe section! Enjoy eating like a VIP!

VIP Superfoods

VIPs eat superfoods that are nutrient dense and pack a punch of VIP POWER!

I'm going to show you how incredibly powerful food can be by giving you a list of JNL-approved super foods and super-food recipes.

Super foods are defined as being nutrient-dense. This means they contain a lot of nutrients, minerals, vitamins, protein, fiber and other things that help your body run much more efficiently. These are foods that you must eat daily for energy and optimal weight loss. These foods help you to maintain mature muscle mass. A great thing about the VIP Food Plan is that you can also make it vegan or vegetarian.

You can do this by substituting the lean meat suggestions for non-meat ones.

List of Super Foods:

TEA: I love to start with liquids because the body is made up of mostly water, and if you're not properly hydrated, your body wont function properly, and plus your largest organ of your body, your skin, won't have that VIP glow!

You should be constantly hydrating your body. So, make sure you drink water, but you can also have a tea party!

Tea has been around for ages. On my trip to China, all the beautiful teahouses amazed me. The indigenous people drink tea five or six times a day and with every meal. This is part of the secret to their longevity. I was amazed by all of the different kinds of tea: green tea, black tea, oolong tea, and white tea. Some were as expensive as my weekly grocery bill! However, you don't need to spend that much to get life boosting results.

Although green tea has a moderate amount of caffeine in its chemical makeup, it also keeps you hydrated. Green tea extract has a substantial effect on weight control, especially during the daytime.

In addition to increasing your metabolism, the tea contributes to a slight increase in energy as well. Most importantly, it's a great source of antioxidants. Plan to drink your tea with meals to increase your metabolism and keep you from eating as much. Healthy liquids keep you fuller in between meals as well.

HIGH FIBER CEREAL: Fiber is your best friend in fighting and winning the war on fat, but very few people get enough fiber in their diet. Fiber also helps you detox, eliminate waste more easily, and feel fuller longer.

High fiber cereals include steel cut oatmeal, which helps lower cholesterol. One of my personal favorites and one that I aim to have every morning is Kellogg's all-Bran Buds cereal. I top about 1/2 cup with blueberries and strawberries, walnuts, and I drizzle it with honey and then I add just enough almond milk to coat the cereal.

WILD FISH: The key here is wild, not farmed. Farmed fish are encaged in their own waste. They also have higher levels of mercury.

Just like adults and people who don't move around a lot, farmed fish are that much fatter and not as healthy. The best wild fish are salmon, which is high in the omega fatty acids which are vital for good brain function. Tilapia is amazing too, as it's a white leaner fish and great for eating when you want to lose fat and gain muscle.

Bee pollen is naturally rich in protein, vitamins, amino acids, and folic acid. Traditionally, it's been consumed to make the immune system stronger. It has over eighteen different amino acids, vitamins, calcium, copper, iron, phosphorus, potassium, fatty acids, carbs, and protein. If you suffer from seasonal allergies, try eating pollen from local bees. Bee pollen is really amazing; it even has a higher amount of protein than any other animal product. The amount of amino acid in bee pollen is higher than that found in dairy products and meat. It has anti-aging benefits and should be used as a natural geriatric remedy. The pollen looks like little yellow specs and can be easily added to any recipe. Try topping your salad with it or stirring it into your salad dressing, blending it into your organic yogurt, mixing it into your morning oatmeal, or sprinkling it over your cut fruit for extra health benefits. Aim to take a teaspoon a day.

Lean red meat, and organic, grass-fed, lean red meat contains amazing vitamins and minerals; you won't find it in fish or even lean poultry: Iron and vitamin B-12, as well as high amounts of protein.

COCONUT OIL: This is one of my favorites: organic, unrefined, virgin coconut oil. If you don't believe me, then listen to this true story. In the early 1970s, there was a surplus in coconut oil. It's very inexpensive and farmers wanted to fatten their cows for prizewinning stock so they tried feeding them coconut oil because it's very calorie dense and high in fat. The cows actually got leaner, more muscular, and had more energy plus increased endurance.

Coconut oil stimulates the thyroid, thus stimulating metabolism, So, you burn fat faster. Think about what this means, healthy fat in, bad fat out. Your need fat to burn fat. I like to put coconut oil in my fruit smoothies and protein shakes. I even pour it over my breakfast cereal. You'll find some great recipes in this book on how you can cook with coconut oil and use it as a condiment.

Finally, the same immune-boosting properties of lauric acid found in breast milk, are also found in coconut oil! What's the first thing that happens when you start losing weight on a diet? You get sick. So, if you are constantly getting sick, you need to boost your immune system. Try taking a tablespoon a day. On my very busy days, I take a tablespoon of coconut oil and I blend it with a teaspoon of bee pollen. This is a nutrient dense super snack that is full of vitamins, minerals, and protein.

NUTS AND SEEDS: Nuts are very healthy and nutritious. In addition to being excellent sources of protein, nuts and seeds contain many other benefits such as vitamins, minerals, fiber, and other chemicals that may prevent cancer and heart disease. Although many people are hesitant to eat nuts because they are high in fat, eating nuts can provide a sense of fullness and satisfaction that causes you to eat less of other high-calorie, high fat foods. Additionally, nuts are high in essential amino acids and healthy fats, making them an important part of any vegan or vegetarian's diet.

WHICH NUTS AND SEEDS ARE BEST?

Walnuts: The walnut is the "king of nuts." Look at them! They kind of look like your brain. Coincidently, it is really great for your brain. Walnuts are high in omega-3 fatty acids, which are essential for proper brain function, mental acuity, and focus.

Almonds: almonds have cholesterol-lowering effects. They also have the ability to reduce your heart disease risk due to the antioxidant action of the vitamin E.

Brazil nuts: Brazil nuts have been linked to preventing breast cancer, due to their high amounts of selenium.

Pistachios: high in iron, protein and fiber with high levels of magnesium, which helps to control blood pressure.

Peanuts: not to be overlooked, this basic nut is an excellent source of B Vitamins, including folate, riboflavin and niacin, helping to reduce muscle degradation and fatigue.

Pumpkin seeds: especially great for men to eat; they protect against prostate cancer.

Sunflower seeds: rich in magnesium, which helps to regulate the nervous system.

Flaxseeds: Flaxseeds are especially fantastic. if you eat them whole, they act like little bristles to your intestines, keeping you more regular.

Ground flaxseeds are also great because you can bake with them. Flax-seed oil is absorbed into your body quickly and makes an excellent addition to any protein shake or fruit smoothie. In Biblical days, oils (including flaxseed, primrose, and olive) were used as a healing topical solution for the skin; they were also ingested for healing properties.

Nut butters: This is a yummy way to eat your nuts. Spread on a rice cake, or drizzle on top of your oatmeal, or a banana.

Cayenne pepper: cayenne pepper acts like a little windmill inside your circulatory system. If you are on medication and feel like it's not working, it's most likely because you've got poor circulation. Make sure that you're including cayenne pepper in your food plan to help increase your circulation and speed up your metabolism. If you have an adverse reaction to hot, spicy foods, take a cayenne pepper capsule.

Pineapple: Fresh chunks of pineapple blended with water make a delicious beverage and act as a natural anti-inflammatory to counteract joint pain and swelling. It also contains a proteolytic enzyme brome-lain, which helps in the digestion of protein. Pineapple can prevent blood clot formation because of its bromelain content. My sons also love this super sticky fruit and I use it in many of my protein shakes and for juicing.

Blueberries: The number one super berry of all time is the blue-berry, a natural antioxidant. Put it in your smoothies, on top of your cereal, or just eat it plain. Blueberries will help you fight off the visible effects of aging.

Sweet potatoes: Sweet potatoes are a staple of the VIP Food Plan. Sweet potatoes contain unique root storage proteins that have been observed to have significant antioxidant capacities. They are full of beta-carotene, vitamin a, and vitamin C. They're also a complex, fibrous carb; so instead of pasta, which is a starchy carb, have a sweet potato.

Brown rice: This is another staple carb of the Mind, Body and Soul diet. It's good fiber and a great source of energy.

Cinnamon: This condiment tastes great and acts as a natural appetite suppressant as well. Put it all over your oatmeal, cereal, and mix it into your coconut oil to put on your morning whole-wheat toast.

Asparagus: If you feel a little bloated, possibly from a high sodium meal the night before, asparagus is a natural diuretic. It's going to help you "pee off the pounds" and rid your body of water weight you're holding onto.

Ginger: In eastern societies, ginger has always been known for its healing powers. It's known to heal and help motion sickness, help deter vomiting, and also help with migraines.

Extra dark chocolate: It's full of antioxidants and it helps boost your mood by releasing serotonin in your brain.

Apples: You can't go wrong with "an apple a day keeps the doctor away." It's high in fiber, and it fills you up. Have an apple before your meal and you'll eat less.

Celery: You burn more calories eating this detoxifying vegetable than not. It actually takes more calories to process the celery, so you burn fat while you eat.

Beets: I especially love to make juice with beets. See the section on juicing in this chapter. Red beet is unique for its high levels of anti-carcinogens and its very high carotenoid content. Red beets are high in carbohydrates and low in fat. It is an excellent source of folic acid.

It is loaded with antioxidants that help the bodyguard against heart disease, certain cancers, especially colon cancer, and even birth defects.

Grapefruit: Grapefruit is an excellent source of vitamin c, a vitamin that helps to support the immune system. This glorious fruit is linked with flushing out fat from the body's system and also is super rich in antioxidants.

Fresh herbs: Seasoning dishes with fresh herbs is a superb way to raise the health benefits of any meal. For instance, parsley outstrips almost all other vegetables in its ability to raise the levels of antioxidants in your body. cilantro helps to lower cholesterol. Find fresh herbs in your produce section, or grow some yourself at home.

Avocados: avocados contain oleic acid, a monounsaturated fat that may help to lower cholesterol. avocados are a good source of potassium, a mineral that helps regulate blood pressure. one cup of avocado has 23% of the daily value for folate, a nutrient important for heart health.

Cold pressed extra virgin olive oil: Pure, extra virgin olive oil is not only a light and delicate addition to many wonderful dishes; it is one of the most health-promoting types of oils available. Olive oil is rich in monounsaturated fat; a type of fat that researchers are discovering has excellent health benefits.

Note: Do not use for frying or sautéing as it produces toxic substances when heated. Rather, use it in cold dishes or drizzle over cooked food.

Tomatoes: Tomatoes contain large amounts of vitamin C, providing 40%of the required daily value. They also contain 15%of the required daily value of vitamin a, 8%of recommended potassium, and 7%of the recommended dietary allowance of iron for women. The red pigment contained in tomatoes is called lycopene, which is an antioxidant, neutralizing free radicals that can damage cells in the body.

Spinach: Spinach contains calcium, thus strengthening the bones. The A and C vitamins in spinach plus the fiber, folic acid, magnesium, and other nutrients help control cancer, especially colon, lung, and breast cancers. Folate also lowers the blood levels of something called homocysteine, a protein that damages arteries. So, spinach also helps protect against heart disease. The flavonoids in spinach help protect against age-related memory loss. Spinach's secret weapon, lutein, makes it one of the best foods in the world to prevent cataracts, as well as age-related macular degeneration, the leading cause of preventable blindness in the elderly. Foods rich in lutein are also thought to help prevent cancer.

Bell peppers: Brightly colored bell peppers, whether green, red, orange, or yellow, are rich sources of some of the best nutrients available. to start, peppers are excellent sources of vitamin C and vitamin A (through its concentration of carotenoids, such as beta-carotene), two very powerful antioxidants. These antioxidants work together to effectively neutralize free radicals, which can travel through the body causing huge amounts of damage to cells.

Barley: Barley is a very good source of fiber and selenium, and a good source of phosphorus, copper, and manganese. It helps boost your elimination to keep you more regular, decreasing the risk of colon cancer and hemorrhoids. Necessary bacteria in the large intestine will also be increased by barley's dietary fiber.

Squash: Pumpkin, acorn, butternut, and spaghetti squash are in the winter squash group. Winter squash provide excellent sources of vitamins B1 and c, folic acid, pantothenic acid, fiber, and potassium, and carotenes. Look for richer colors as this denotes a higher concentration of these nutrients. Winter squash exert a protective effect against many cancers, particularly lung cancer. diets that are rich in carotenes (especially pumpkins) offer protection against cancer, heart disease, and type-2 diabetes. Choose winter squash over summer since summer squash have high water content; they are not as nutrient-dense as the winter varieties. However, summer squash still provides several nutritional benefits. They are low in calories and provide a decent amount of vitamin c, potassium, and carotenes.

Garlic: Garlic has long been considered an herbal miracle drug. Modern science has shown that garlic is a powerful natural antibiotic, albeit broad-spectrum rather than targeted. The body does not appear to build up resistance to the garlic, so it's positive health benefits continue over time. The smartest way to eat garlic is by taking it as a supplement to avoid bad breath. Or you can also cook with it to soften its flavor and odor.

Olives: olives are a staple in the Mediterranean diet, known for their amazing health benefits. Olives are high in monounsaturated fats and are rich in vitamin e. Vitamin e is the body's main fat-soluble antioxidant, neutralizing free radicals in the body which are rich in fat. When monounsaturated fats are stable and the body has sufficient vitamin e, this adds to cellular processes like energy production. So, grab a few olives a day by simply adding them to your salads, or enjoy with your anti-pasta dishes.

Horseradish: Due to its antibiotic properties, horseradish can cure urinary tract infections and kill bacteria in the throat that cause bronchitis, coughs, and related problems. I love it with my lean steaks for added health punch!

The Power of Juicing

> *"Life is good! Squeeze every*
> *bit of goodness out of it!"*
>
> — *J N L*

I'm here to tell you, as a health advocate and a fitness expert, that the typical two-week-long, extreme detoxing regimens just don't work to help you lose weight. When you go on a solely juice/vinegar/molasses concoction detox, you slow down your metabolism because you're not getting solid food, and you're hoarding the fat that you already have. Your body senses that it's starving, so it holds onto your fat by slowing down your metabolism. Not only that, you're losing precious muscle tone and gaining more fat. Don't believe those twenty-one-day detox diet claims. Your body needs food to function. I do, however, believe in juicing and drinking a glass every day with your food plan. It's a fast and efficient way to get amazing amount of vitamins and minerals that are easily assimilated into your body; plus, it's great for your kids. When they were little my sons loved to watch how the juicer instantly pulls the juice out of an apple. It is beneficial and fun to work in a glass of fresh juice!

THE ENDLESS BENEFITS OF DRINKING FRESHLY MADE VEGETABLE AND FRUIT JUICE

Let's face it, we all need to eat more fruits and vegetables. However, it's time consuming and difficult to prepare and eat our suggested daily servings. Juicing makes it easy to consume vegetables that are hard to eat, like spinach and even broccoli. Speaking of vegetables, when you juice them with sweet oranges or apples, they just taste so much better, and are a lot more refreshing. Think about it, would you prefer to eat a bowl of steamed carrots? Or would you rather juice one with some apples and pineapple, and then enjoy it in a tall glass over ice? That's the secret. Juicing is a way to deliciously "sneak" in more fresh fruits and vegetables. Consuming fruits and vegetables this way is just so much more pleasing. Here's the great thing about it; you can juice anything, fruit or vegetable! The combinations are endless. You can get as creative as you want and you can have fun with it. Improve the quality of your lifestyle by juicing daily. Trust me, there is nothing like a tall, cold glass of freshly juiced apples, grapefruit, oranges, carrots, lemons, pomegranates, blueberries, strawberries, beets, ginger, pears, celery, cucumber, and parsley... okay—you get the idea! Check my recipe section for great VIP juicing recipes.

VIP Food Plan and Recipes

The main goals of the VIP Food Plan are to nourish all three parts of the triad—the mind the body and the soul. This helps you lose weight, gain strength, and to feel and look your best.

RULE NUMBER ONE: You must eat at least five to six times a day.

Breakfast: Start off with what should be both the most important and the largest meal of the day, breakfast. If you like to work out on an empty stomach, go for it! But remember to eat within the one-hour time frame post workout. During sleep, you are at rest and, of course, not eating. Breakfast, or your post workout meal, should be the largest meal of the day. in order to work with your metabolism instead of against it, make sure you trickle your calories down throughout the day, with dinner as your smallest meal.

Mid-morning snack: Around 10:30am it's important to refuel with a small mid-morning snack to keep your energy level high. Aim to consume around two hundred calories of a little protein. However, if you train on an empty stomach first thing in the morning, make sure you eat right after your workout, as I have previously mentioned.

VIP FIT TIP:
Make it a goal to not eat carbs after 4:00pm—you'll see major results! You can eat all of the fibrous carbs (vegetables and salad) you want, but steer away from the complex and simple carbs (brown rice, breads, pastas, etc.). You will wake up feeling thinner with more energy.

Lunch: Lunch should never be skipped! I always hear my clients state that they just can't break away from work to eat lunch because they don't have time, or they don't feel hungry. I can't stress enough how important it is to eat lunch. If you skip lunch, you are setting yourself up to sabotage your food plan. You will end up eating more later on in the day. You will also be more prone to eat high sugar and high carb foods later on. You're more likely to eat in the night if you skip lunch. Lunch needs to be a combination of lean protein, good-for-you whole grain carbs, a little heart-healthy fat, and fibrous carbs.

Late Afternoon Snack: Eating your late afternoon snack is like insurance. It will help you to not overeat at dinner and also keep your sugar levels even, so you don't binge later on. Eating a small, balanced two hundred-calorie snack around three or four o'clock will help you to keep your energy up, while helping you to not eat the whole grain carb at dinner.

Dinner: Dinner is a time to sit and relax with your family and friends. Value this time to eat together as a family and unwind from the busy day. Stick with your food plan, even if you see that others are not, this is especially important during dinnertime. The main focus here is to eat a lean source of protein with a heart healthy fat, along with some fibrous carbs, while staying away from complex carbs. Also, aim at only engaging in low-key, happy subjects to keep all negative or overwhelming topics at bay, which could trigger an emotional eating splurge or wanting to open up that bottle of wine, which is full of sugar and empty calories. The alcohol shuts down your metabolism, as it has to stop everything to break down the alcohol first, and then go back to burning off your food.

If you are still hungry after dinner, and you find that you can't go to sleep because of your hunger pains, quiet them down with a small low-carb, high protein pre-bedtime snack. I highly recommend a rich delicious protein shake made with water to satiate and quiet down your growling tummy. I prefer a pre-bedtime protein shake, because it replenishes my energy without causing me to gain weight, plus it hydrates my body since its water based. It also helps me to repair my muscle tone while I am sleeping. The best part, is that they are rich and delicious, almost like a good-for-you smoothie or "milk shake." other healthy pre-bedtime snack options will be found in the two-week sample menu section. Take the small amount of time to "set yourself up for success" by pre-planning and preparing your meals ahead of time so you will stop eating accidentally.

VIP FIT TIP:

One main reason for people eating heavy meals in the night is that they were "good all day," meaning they ate either too little or not enough. So, make sure, that you concentrate on eating breakfast, your mid-morning snack, and lunch to ensure that you won't overeat at night.

VIP FIT TIP:

Have whole grain carbs at lunch, but not at dinner. If you are eating a grilled chicken salad for lunch, and then a pan-seared fish fillet with a sweet potato and steamed asparagus for dinner, switch these two meals around. Have what you typically have for lunch for dinner, and then what you have for dinner at lunch. Your lunch needs to be larger in portion than your dinner. Aim to have a complex carb with lunch during the day, and to exclude it at night.

Making this simple switch will help you lose weight and to have more energy during the day, thus allowing you not to hit that late afternoon slump.

VIP FOOD PLAN AND RECIPES

Two-Week Sample Menu:

DAY 1

Breakfast—eggs Florentine in a Warm Whole Grain Pita Pocket

Midmorning Snack— Super Banana Split Protein Shake

Lunch—Sicilian Protein-Packed antipasto

Late Afternoon Snack—handful of unsalted nuts— blend of walnuts

Dinner—cayenne chicken coconut Thai Soup

Pre-Bedtime Snack—snack size cup of low-carb plain yogurt topped with fresh berries.

DAY 2

Breakfast—2 Whole Grain toaster waffles, topped with sliced bananas and walnuts, drizzled with honey.

Midmorning Snack—Vanilla coconut Protein Shake

Lunch—6-inch turkey Subway sandwich, with all the vegetables, snack size of crunch-pack apples, bottled water. (hint: steer clear of the mayo, and you will make your lunch just that much healthier!)

Late Afternoon Snack—twelve almonds with a small apple.

Dinner—lemongrass coconut chicken hot entrée from Kashi.

Pre-Bedtime Snack—Small tin of tuna, rinsed, with a touch of fat free mayo & relish.

DAY 3

Breakfast—Blueberry Protein Pancakes

Midmorning Snack—German chocolate cake Protein Shake

Lunch—Barley Vegetable Salad with Feta

Late Afternoon Snack—Snack size cottage cheese topped with sliced bananas, drizzled with honey.

Dinner—Grilled Grapefruit Marinated chicken breasts with avocado

Pre-Bedtime Snack— Protein Shake—one scoop with 6-8 oz. of water.

DAY 4

Breakfast—egg white omelet with side of whole wheat toast.

Midmorning Snack—Super Berry Blast Protein Smoothie with coconut oil

Lunch—Grilled chicken breast with sweet potato.

Late Afternoon Snack—Sliced banana topped with two tbsp. of almond butter with handful of whole grain pretzels.

Dinner—Grilled salmon breast squeezed with lemon, side of steamed asparagus and green house salad.

Pre-Bedtime Snack—2 hardboiled eggs with yolks removed, dashed with white pepper.

DAY 5

Breakfast—Southwest Veggie omelet with a Side of Whole Wheat toast

Midmorning Snack—key lime Pie Protein Shake

Lunch—Italian turkey Meatballs, Sicilian Style

Late Afternoon Snack—Small apple with 1 serving of string cheese.

Dinner—roasted red peppers in olive oil with garlic shrimp.

Pre-Bedtime Snack—Strawberries and low-carb vanilla yogurt.

DAY 6

Breakfast—Plain fat free yogurt, swirl in 1 tbsp. sugar free pre-serves, 1/4 cup Grape nuts, and a tsp of local bee pollen.

Midmorning Snack—coconut cookies with a side of Fat-Free cottage cheese

Lunch—turkey & low-fat Swiss cheese sandwich on sprouted bread, small apple and bottle of water.

Late Afternoon Snack—cut up crudités with drizzled hummus.

Dinner—Shake 'n Bake chicken breasts with broiled tomatoes, side green house salad.

Pre-Bedtime Snack—Small fat-free snack size cottage cheese with strawberries and blueberries.

DAY 7

Breakfast—Fortified French toast topped with Bananas Foster

Midmorning Snack—exotic chai tea Protein Shake

Lunch—oriental Beef Bowl with Stir Fry Vegetables Served over hot Brown rice

Late Afternoon Snack—2 whole grain crackers and 2 tablespoons Saba roasted eggplant.

Dinner—Baked Blackened Salmon Steaks with Mango and Black Bean Salsa

Pre-Bedtime Snack—2 Quick deviled eggs—take 2 hardboiled eggs, slice in half, discard one yolk. Quickly mash the one remaining yolk with a little touch of fat free mayo. top egg white halves with mixture, dash with black pepper.

DAY 8

Breakfast——Pizza for breakfast? Why not! Toast a split English muffin, top with 2 slices of tomato and low-fat mozzarella cheese.

Place under grill for a few minutes, and you have a nutritious breakfast.

Midmorning Snack—Winter Squash Soup with Slice of Swiss cheese on Whole Grain roll

Lunch—Quick and easy cucumber & turkey Sandwiches—spread 2 slices of sprouted bread with low-fat cream cheese, cucumber slices, reduced fat feta cheese, and a few slices of deli turkey for added protein.

Late Afternoon Snack—Slices of low-fat Swiss cheese on whole grain crackers with low sodium turkey slices.

Dinner—Grilled Mahi Mahi, with any of your favorite Mrs. Dash seasonings, with a side of sautéed spinach drizzled with olive oil and lemon.

Pre-Bedtime Snack—chunks of cantaloupe wrapped in prosciutto.

DAY 9

Breakfast—cottage cheese with exotic Fruits drizzled with coconut oil

Midmorning Snack—cookies and cream Protein Shake

Lunch—curry chicken Walnut Cranberry Salad, Served open Faced on Whole Grain

Late Afternoon Snack—Small 6-inch, low-carb, whole grain tortilla with roast beef slices, rolled up.

Dinner—Succulent exotic Asian lettuce Wraps

Pre-Bedtime Snack—Walnut and Strawberry Ricotta Whip mix all ingredients together, drizzle with honey and enjoy: 1/2 cup of part skim ricotta cheese, 1/4 cup walnuts, 1/4 tsp almond extract.

DAY 10

Breakfast——Berry Blend—a cinch to make! 1 snack size cottage cheese, 1/2 cup of mixed berries—mix together and then top onto 2 slices of whole wheat toast.

Midmorning Snack—chocolate Peanut Butter Supreme Protein Shake

Lunch—Sunflower Seed chicken Wrap—take one low-carb whole grain wrap, top with grilled chicken slices, black olives, sprinkle some sunflower seeds for extra crunch, spinach and diced tomatoes. Wrap and enjoy!

Late Afternoon Snack—Snack size cottage cheese topped with fresh blueberries.

Dinner—Quick and healthy Sliced Beef Salad—cook steak slices, tomatoes, and purple onion together in a large skillet—douse it with a touch of balsamic vinegar and olive oil—top hot meat and tomatoes and onion mixture over a bed of greens.

Pre-Bedtime Snack—Four medium size precooked shrimp dipped in cocktail sauce.

DAY 11

Breakfast—Breakfast Burrito with avocado on Whole-Grain low-carb tortilla

Midmorning Snack—island Pina colada Passion Shake

Lunch—tuna Salad in Pita served with Sprouts and Spinach

Late Afternoon Snack—nut Butter toast with crunchy Pears—toast 1 slice of sprouted bread, spread with nut butter, top with cashews for extra crunch, and then layer on slices of ripe pear drizzle with honey.

Dinner—Filet Mignon with lemon Pepper asparagus

Pre-Bedtime Snack—1 wedge of laughing cow cheese and a handful of grapes.

DAY 12

Breakfast—"Speedy Gonzalez" egg and Bean tostada—whip up some egg white in a skillet, mix in some pinto or black beans, top with some low- fat cheese and diced tomato—top this mixture onto a corn tostada. For extra fat burning—add a few hot Chilis or a few dashes of tabasco.

Midmorning Snack—Mochaccino Protein Shake

Lunch—Quick Fix Barbecued Fajitas by Kraft—for a stress free fiesta, you can make chicken and vegetable fajitas. use pre-cooked chicken tenders to save you time. in a large skillet sauté, some sliced red bell pepper and white onion. add about 1/2 tbs. Kraft original barbeque sauce for added smoky flavor. add chicken and cook for about 2 more minutes, until the chicken is well heated top onto whole wheat low-carb tortillas, like Tumaro's.

Late Afternoon Snack—diced pear topped with walnuts and a dash of cinnamon.

Dinner—Maple and Mustard Glazed Salmon—mix 2 tablespoons of maple syrup and 2 tablespoons of coarse brown mustard. Coat salmon, and cook in broiler at 400 degrees until done. Serve with steamed asparagus with a squeeze of lemon.

Pre-Bedtime Snack—Apple Pie à la Mode Protein Shake

DAY 13

Breakfast—Warm Walnut cinnamon apple oatmeal, on page 102

Midmorning Snack—chocolate-covered cherry Protein Shake

Lunch—chicken tortilla Soup topped with avocado

Late Afternoon Snack—olive cheese Melts—take a toasted whole grain English muffin split in two, drizzle with cold pressed extra virgin olive oil, top with slices of tomato, fresh basil and sprinkle shredded low-fat mozzarella cheese and black olives. Broil for about one minute until cheese melts.

Dinner—Caribbean Shrimp and Mango Salad—easy to make and hard to resist

Pre-Bedtime Snack—turkey and low-Fat Swiss cheese rollup—take 1 slice of carved sandwich sliced turkey breast and one slice of low-fat Swiss cheese. top the cheese on the turkey and roll up. optional—a touch of cranberry sauce, or even some course ground mustard.

DAY 14

Breakfast—Quinoa cereal with Fresh Fruit. top cooked quinoa with pumpkin seeds, sliced almonds, and your favorite berries. Mix in 1 tbsp. of coconut oil. top with 1 tbsp. of bee pollen. drizzle with honey.

Midmorning Snack—low-carb Flaxseed and nut Granola Snack

Lunch—Asian turkey Burgers

Late Afternoon Snack—The Turtle Shake, on page 118

Dinner—Shrimp & avocado Salad—toss all ingredients and place inside a sliced open avocado: 1 cup cooked shrimp, 2 hardboiled eggs, 1/2 cup chopped celery, 1/4 c. chopped green onions, 1/4 cup chopped parsley, 1/2 c. chopped cucumber. 1/4 c. chopped bell pepper, 4 tbsp. light mayonnaise, 2 tsp hot sweet mustard, lemon and pepper to taste.

Pre-Bedtime Snack—Beautiful Berry Blast Protein Shake

The VIP Recipes

When creating these recipes, I kept in mind, the delicate balance of taste, the ease of preparation, the utilization of Super foods, plus blending in antioxidant rich foods and heart healthy fats. Enjoy the pleasure of healthy foods again by making these simple, easy-to-whip-up meals. Re-awaken your "inner chef" by making it fun and including your children and family in the preparation process.

Breakfast Recipes

EGGS FLORENTINE IN A WARM WHOLE GRAIN PITA POCKET

This is a healthy take on an old-time classic. Feel free to add sliced tomato.

Ingredients

1 cup fresh spinach

Small clove of garlic, chopped

1 whole egg, 3 egg whites

2 tbsp. reduced fat feta cheese, crumbled

half of a whole-grain low-carb pita pocket

Directions

Place a lightly coated nonstick pan with cooking spray over medium heat. add garlic and then spinach. Sauté until it wilts. Whisk eggs until blended. Pour over the spinach, and cook to your liking. top with cheese. Then place inside your pita for a quick yet filling breakfast on the go.

BLUEBERRY PROTEIN PANCAKES

These are so fun to make with your younger children, as they love to add the berries while the pancakes are cooking. You can substitute the blueberries for any other berry you desire, or even use sliced banana. Sometimes I even replace the berries for chocolate morsels and make chocolate pancakes, to enjoy the healthy benefits of chocolate. You won't even need syrup on these because they will be so naturally sweet.

Ingredients

1 scoop of Vanilla Protein Powder

2 egg whites

1/2 cup of blueberries

Directions

Spray and heat skillet. Whip protein powder and eggs together. Pour batter onto skillet. let one side cook while you add blueberries on top. Flip pancakes to cook the other side.

SOUTHWEST VEGGIE OMELET WITH A SIDE OF WHOLE WHEAT TOAST

Enjoy the health and beauty benefits of spinach, bell peppers, and eggs all in one super zesty dish. Serve with a side of whole-wheat toast for a complete energizing breakfast.

Ingredients:

3/4 cups of your favorite veggies suitable for an omelet (I suggest spinach, onion, mushrooms, bell peppers)

touch of freshly minced garlic (optional)

a handful of cherry tomatoes cut in half

3 egg whites, one whole egg

dash of black pepper

dash of cayenne pepper

Sprinkle of shredded Mexican cheese

Directions

Coat nonstick pan with cooking spray and place over medium heat. Whisk eggs. add all vegetables and sauté.

Pour eggs over into the pan and scramble lightly. Cook until done.

Enjoy with a slice of low-carb toast.

FORTIFIED FRENCH TOAST TOPPED WITH BANANAS FOSTER

Making French toast with protein powder will keep you feeling fuller longer. Top with my healthier version of Bananas Foster for a breakfast you will be jumping out of bed for and will never want to miss!

Ingredients

1 whole egg, 3 egg whites

4 slices of low-carb multi-grain bread

1/2 tsp of cinnamon

1 scoop of BSN's Fresh cinnamon roll lean dessert

Protein Powder

Topping: one sliced banana, 2 tbsp. of maple syrup.

Directions

Whisk the eggs together in a medium size bowl. Add the protein powder and stir until smooth. Add cinnamon to mixture. Dip the bread, thoroughly coating each side. Spray a nonstick skillet with cooking spray and place on medium heat. Place the protein-coated bread into the frying pan. Cook until golden brown about three minutes.

Topping: lightly coat a small nonstick skillet with butter-flavored cooking spray and place over medium heat. Add sliced bananas and fry for about one minute.

TROPICAL COTTAGE CHEESE WITH EXOTIC FRUITS DRIZZLED WITH COCONUT OIL

This is a great breakfast to whip up when you are in a hurry. It's tropical in flavor and texture because of the sweet pineapple and coconut oil.

Ingredients

Small snack-size portion of cottage cheese

Fruit of your choice, try blueberries or pineapple

1 tsp of bee pollen

Whole grain English muffin

1 tbsp. of coconut oil

Directions

Toast English muffin. Blend bee pollen and fruit into cottage cheese. Top English muffin with mixture. Drizzle with coconut oil on top.

BREAKFAST BURRITO WITH AVOCADO ON WHOLE-GRAIN LOW-CARB TORTILLA

Wake up your taste buds in the morning with this meal that sends your mouth on a vacation south of the border! You will make your mouth say "ole!"

Ingredients

1 8-inch whole-wheat low-carb tortilla

1 whole egg, 3 egg whites

1/4 cup black beans or pinto beans

Sprinkle of shredded reduced fat Mexican cheese

one small tomato, diced

half of one small avocado

Directions

Lightly coat a nonstick skillet with cooking spray. Place over medium heat. Warm up the tortilla by placing it in skillet, turning over after thirty seconds on each side. Set aside.

Beat eggs and pour into skillet. Cook until done, then add to skillet your tomato, beans, and cheese. Put eggs onto warmed tortilla and then top with avocado. Fold tortilla and enjoy.

WARM WALNUT CINNAMON APPLE OATMEAL

Start your day off right with a hearty breakfast, full of rich texture that will stick to your ribs! The added protein powder will fortify your warm cereal with protein for a balanced breakfast.

Ingredients

1/2 cup of instant oatmeal

1 cup of hot water

1 scoop of Vanilla Protein Powder

Small apple, cored and sliced into wedges

1 tbsp. of coconut oil

1/4 cup of walnuts

dash of cinnamon

Directions

In skillet, warm up coconut oil and place apple wedges and walnuts in pan. add a dash of cinnamon. Cook for about three minutes until apples get soft. In a bowl place oatmeal and water. Place in microwave for thirty seconds, stirring when done. Top with apples and walnut mixture.

Midmorning Snacks

VANILLA COCONUT PROTEIN SHAKE

Ingredients

one scoop of Vanilla Protein Powder,

1 tbsp. of coconut oil

1 tsp of bee pollen

1 tbsp. of ground flax seed

1 tbsp. of coconut flakes (optional)

3 cubes of ice

8 ounces of water

Blend and enjoy.

SUPER BERRY BLAST PROTEIN SMOOTHIE WITH COCONUT OIL

Vitamin c and photochemical rich sweet berries, swirled into your creamy vanilla shake with an essence of tropical coconuts—this power drink will send you into heaven!

Ingredients

one scoop of Vanilla

Protein Powder

1/2 cup of mixed berries (strawberries, blueberries, raspberries, blackberries)

1 tsp of bee pollen

1 tbsp. of ground flaxseed

3 cubes of ice

8 ounces of water

Blend and enjoy

COCONUT COOKIES WITH SIDE OF FAT FREE COTTAGE CHEESE

They sound sinful, but they're not! They are great for you because they are low in sugar, high in fiber, and the flaxseeds add texture and are a great source of essential fatty acids. What a great, guilt-free energy boosting treat! enjoy with a snack-size fat-free cottage cheese.

Ingredients

1 cup unsweetened coconut flakes

3 tbsp. warm water

1 whole egg

1 tbsp. honey

1 tsp coconut oil

1/4 cup flaxseeds

1 cup old-fashioned oats

Directions

Mix warm water and honey together. Add coconut flakes. Beat in the egg. Mix thoroughly. Form into balls and drop by spoonful on well-greased cookie sheet. Bake at 400 degrees for twelve to fifteen minutes.

WINTER SUPER SQUASH SOUP WITH SLICE OF SWISS CHEESE ON WHOLE GRAIN ROLL

Squash is loaded with vitamin c (great for boosting your immune system and to fight off colds) and fiber (to keep you regular). The cayenne is great for circulation, and the coconut oil has medicinal properties to fight off infections and stimulate the thyroid. But you won't even think of this soup as your typical "healthy meal" because of how rich and satisfying it is!

Ingredients

3⁄4 Spanish onion

Small clove of garlic, minced, or use minced garlic in jar

2 tsp coconut oil

1 tsp curry powder

1 dash of cinnamon

1⁄2 tsp cayenne pepper

4 cups reduced sodium non-fat chicken or vegetable broth

5 large winter squash, baked until soft

1 sweet potato, baked until semi-soft then cubed

dash of black pepper

topping: fat free sour cream and whole-wheat croutons

Directions

In large saucepan, sauté onion and garlic. Add black and cayenne pepper, stirring to coat. Add broth, sweet potatoes, squash, and bring to a boil. Reduce heat to medium, partially cover, and cook for about seven to ten minutes. Remove from heat, top with a dollop of sour cream and whole wheat croutons.

CHOCOLATE PEANUT BUTTER SUPREME PROTEIN SHAKE

Satisfyingly thick, rich, and super creamy, this shake will stop hunger in its tracks without blowing your food plan.

Ingredients

8 ounces of cold water

one scoop of Vanilla Protein Powder,

chocolate Fudge Pudding Flavor

1 tbsp. natural no sugar added/no trans-fat peanut butter

3 ice cubes

Directions

Blend and enjoy!

MOCHACCINO PROTEIN SHAKE

I usually make this with leftover cold coffee that is left in the pot from breakfast. or you can use instant coffee instead. it's an energy booster that's rich and creamy!

Ingredients

one scoop of Vanilla/Chocolate/or Mocha Coffee Flavored Protein Shake Powder

8 ounces of cold water

1/4 cup of cold coffee or 2 tsp of instant coffee granules

Directions
Blend and enjoy!

LOW-CARB FLAXSEED AND NUT GRANOLA

A treat that I created that my entire family loves to whip up together and eat!

Ingredients

1 cup flaxseed

1 cup sunflower seeds, unsalted

1 cup unsweetened shredded coconut

1 cup each chopped pecans, walnuts, and almonds

1/2 cup of coconut oil, melted

2 tsp cinnamon

2 tsp Protein Powder, Whipped

Vanilla Flavor

Directions

In a large roasting pan, mix the flaxseeds, sunflower seeds, coconut, and nuts. Drizzle with the melted coconut oil. Stir in cinnamon, vanilla protein powder. Toast in the oven at 325 degrees for thirty minutes. Stir every five to ten minutes.

VIP FIT TIP: This recipe gives you six servings. I suggest that you prepare it and then portion it out into six plastic sandwich bags for a portable treat to take on the go.

Lunch Recipes

SICILIANO PROTEIN-PACKED ANTIPASTO

Being Italian, my parents frequently prepared a large platter of delicious cheeses, meats, veggies, and olives. This dish makes for an interesting and fun lunch that is just as pleasing to the eye as it is to the tummy!

Here is my healthy version in honor of them.

Ingredients

lean cuts of sliced turkey breast, roast beef, and prosciutto

Black and green olives, rinsed off to remove excess salt

low fat Swiss cheese

low fat mozzarella cheese

cherry tomatoes cut in half

Broccoli florets and carrot sticks

dash of minced fresh Italian herbs such as oregano, basil, parsley, sage, or rosemary

Whole wheat bread

Directions

On a plate, beautifully arrange all the ingredients for a delectable presentation.

VIP FIT TIP: Rinse the olives and meats with cold water to remove unnecessary salt. Feel free to drizzle the veggies with olive oil for an extra added health benefit.

BARLEY VEGETABLE SALAD WITH FETA

Hands down, barley is one of the best whole grains for you because it carries more fiber than brown rice. Barley is also high in viscous soluble fiber, which helps to lower LDL cholesterol, the so-called "bad" cholesterol thus reducing the risk factor of heart disease. Barley is usually used in soups or stews but I like to use it to "beef" up a delicious vegetable salad sprinkled with feta. Dig in with no guilt!

Ingredients

1 cup cooked hulled barley

1 cup water

1 green or red bell pepper, seeded and diced

1 1/2 cups chopped carrots

1 cup red cabbage

1/2 cup minced red onion

1/4 cup minced sundried tomatoes

1 tbsp. red wine vinegar

2 tsp creamed horseradish

1 tsp olive oil

coarsely ground black pepper to taste

dash of cayenne pepper

2 tbsp. of feta cheese (optional)

Directions

Cook hulled barley. Put in large mixing bowl; add green or red bell pepper, carrots, cabbage, tomatoes, and onion. In a small bowl, mix together vinegar, horseradish, and oil. Pour over barley mixture and stir to coat. top with feta cheese. Season with black and cayenne pepper.

VIP FIT TIP: This is an excellent zesty vegetarian salad. Feel free to omit the feta if you are on a vegan diet. Also, the horseradish in this dish helps to fight off colds and clears your sinuses if you are congested.

ITALIAN TURKEY MEATBALLS, SICILIAN STYLE

One of my favorite childhood memories was warming up with a big bowl of homemade spaghetti and meatballs. Here is my modern day version. I swapped out the ground beef for low fat turkey, slashing the calories while keeping the protein high. As for the pasta, use whole wheat or spinach pasta to up the fiber. Yes, you can have carbs, but the right ones. Enjoy one cup of pasta and two meatballs to keep in line with your portion control. As we say in Italian, mangi!

Ingredients

Cooking spray

1 lb. antibiotic-free ground turkey

1 slice whole wheat bread, crust removed pulsed into crumbs

1/4 cup grated Parmesan

1/2 grated carrot

2 large cloves of garlic, minced

2 tbsp. minced parsley

2 tsp minced fresh thyme leaves

1 egg lightly beaten

1/2 teaspoon salt

Freshly ground black pepper

1 box whole wheat pasta

Directions

In a 4-quart saucepan heat the oil over medium heat. Sauté the onions until translucent, about three minutes, then add the garlic and cook for one minute more. Add tomato paste, tomatoes, oregano, rosemary, and salt. Bring all the ingredients to a low boil, reduce heat and cook for approximately fifteen minutes, until liquid has evaporated slightly. Season with salt and pepper, to taste. While sauce is cooking, make meatballs. Preheat the broiler. Spray a baking sheet with cooking spray. Combine the turkey with all other ingredients, except for the fresh basil, in a large work bowl. Form into two and a half inch balls and place on a baking sheet. Broil for ten minutes, or until browned and almost entirely cooked through. Meanwhile, remove rosemary sprig from sauce and add fresh basil. Add the meatballs to the sauce, cover, and cook an additional ten minutes, or until sauce has slightly thickened and meatballs have absorbed some of the sauce. While the meatballs are cooking, cook the whole wheat spaghetti according to package directions.

Drain the pasta and return it to the pot. Add the sauce and meatballs, toss and heat through over medium heat. Divide evenly among four pasta bowls and garnish with parsley and one tablespoon grated Parmesan.

ORIENTAL BEEF BOWL WITH STIR FRY VEGETABLES OVER HOT BROWN RICE

Take a VIP trip to the orient with this exotic and succulent recipe. Don't let its complexity fool you, as it's a cinch to prepare.

Ingredients

    1 pound beef flank steak, well-trimmed

    2 tbsp. oriental dark-roasted sesame oil, divided

    2 tbsp. reduced-sodium soy sauce

    1 1/2 tsp raw brown sugar

    1 tsp cornstarch

    1/4 tsp crushed red pepper pods

    2 cloves garlic, crushed

    1 tbsp. fresh ginger, minced

    1 small red pepper cut into 1" pieces

1 small can whole baby corn

4 ounces snow pea pods, julienned

2 tbsp. chopped parsley

Directions

Partially freeze beef flank steak to firm (approx. 30 minutes). Cut steak in half lengthwise; cut each half across the grain into eighth-inch strips. combine one tablespoon sesame oil, soy sauce, sugar and cornstarch; pour over beef strips, tossing to coat. heat remaining sesame oil in wok or large nonstick skillet over medium/high heat. add pepper pods, garlic and ginger; cook thirty seconds. Add pepper and corn; stir-fry ninety seconds. add pea pods; stir-fry thirty seconds. Remove vegetables from pan; reserve.

Stir-fry beef strips (half at a time) two to three minutes. return vegetables and beef to pan and heat through. top with fresh parsley for added antioxidants.

VIP FIT TIP: Invest in a rice cooker, which will help you to always have a healthy complex carb on hand without the cooking. You simply add water and brown rice, and shut the lid. The cooker will prepare brown rice and keep it fresh for at least three days.

CURRY CHICKEN WALNUT CRANBERRY SALAD, SERVED OPEN FACED ON WHOLE GRAIN

Make over your old-fashioned chicken salad with my new innovative version that has added crunch from the celery and walnuts. Make this batch large to save for leftovers.

Ingredients

4 large skinless boneless chicken breasts, cooked and diced

1 stalk celery chopped

1 small apple, cored and cut into small chunks

1 cup seedless red grapes

1/2 cup walnuts

dash of white pepper

1/2 teaspoon of curry powder

3/4 cup light or fat free mayonnaise

1/2 cup dried cranberries

Directions

In a large salad bowl combine the chicken, celery, onion, apple, cranberries, grapes, walnuts, pepper, curry powder, and mayonnaise. Mix all together, tossing to coat. Salad is ready to serve with your toasted whole wheat roll. Feel free to add a slice or two of tomato and some fresh spinach leaves to up your vitamins and antioxidants to this meal.

TUNA SALAD IN PITA SERVED WITH SPROUTS AND SPINACH

Ingredients

1/2 cup chopped red pepper

1/4 cup bottled pickled vegetables, drained and chopped

1/4 cup finely chopped red onion

1/4 cup fat-free mayonnaise

1 (12-ounce) can albacore tuna in water, drained and flaked

2 tsp fresh minced parsley

2 cups of spinach

alfalfa sprouts

Directions

Combine the first six ingredients in a medium bowl. Scoop a half cup tuna salad into four pitas. top each with spinach and a few threads of alfalfa sprouts.

CHICKEN TORTILLA SOUP TOPPED WITH AVOCADO

Full of low fat protein, essential fatty acids from the avocado and the citrus punch of the lime make this soup a show-stopper.

Ingredients

3 medium-sized cans of fat-free chicken broth

1/2 bunch of washed and chopped cilantro

1-2 ripe avocados peeled and sliced into small chunks

3 tiny pinches of thyme

1 pinch of marjoram

1 tbsp. of onion

1 block of skimmed mozzarella cheese (80 calories per ounce)

Whole grain tortilla chips

2 small limes, seeded and diced into wedges

1 small package of chicken tenders

White pepper, if desired

dash of cayenne

Directions

Empty the chicken broth and chopped cilantro into a large kettle or pot, adding two cans of water, the onion, thyme, and marjoram. cook on medium heat. Spray a skillet or pan with nonstick cooking spray and cook chicken slowly so that it caramelizes on both sides.

When chicken is done, cut into bite-sized chunks and transfer to the broth. Cook until hot but not bubbly. Toss in the diced, seeded limes, leaving on the rinds. The rinds add a citrus punch to the soup, plus the soup will have a more exotic presentation. Top each bowl with crushed up tortilla chips, the avocado and a sprinkle of cheese.

VIP FIT TIP: Coat the chunked avocado with some of the lime juice to prevent browning.

Late Afternoon Snacks

- Twelve almonds with a small apple.

- Sliced banana topped with two tablespoons of almond butter, with handful of whole-grain pretzels

- cut up crudités with hummus

- Slices of low-fat Swiss cheese on whole grain crackers with low sodium turkey slices

- Snack-size fat-free cottage cheese topped with fresh blueberries

- Diced pear topped with walnuts and a dash of cinnamon

THE TURTLE SHAKE

One of my favorites, this whimsical take on the famous chocolate, pecan, and soft caramel treat is impossible to resist!

Ingredients

1 scoop Chocolate Protein Shake,

1 ounce pecan halves, chopped

2 tbsp. natural peanut butter

3 ice cubes

1 tbsp. sugar-free and fat-free caramel syrup

Blend and enjoy!

Dinner

CAYENNE CHICKEN COCONUT THAI SOUP

It's known that soup fills you up, thus quickly cutting your appetite. Make a whole pot and freeze individual portions. You can also bring this soup with you to work and warm it up in the microwave for a hot, delicious snack that will fill you up—and not with guilt! it's also a great soup to make if you feel a cold coming on. The cayenne helps to fight off fever, and the coconut oil boosts your immune system.

Ingredients

1 tsp coconut oil

1 tbsp. unsalted butter

1 clove garlic chopped

4 shallots, chopped

2 small fresh red chili peppers, chopped

1 cup red pepper, sliced lengthwise

1 cup broccoli

1 tbsp. chopped lemongrass

3 cups chicken stock

6 ounces lean chicken breast cut into bite size chunks

1 1/2 cups unsweetened coconut milk

1 bunch fresh basil leaves

Directions

In a medium saucepan, heat oil and butter. Sauté the garlic, shallots, chilies, red pepper, broccoli, and lemongrass in oil until fragrant. Stir in chicken stock, coconut milk, and bring almost to a boil. Simmer on low heat until chicken is cooked. Add some cayenne at this point. Make it as hot and spicy as you like. You can go wild or mild, it's your choice!

GRILLED GRAPEFRUIT MARINATED CHICKEN BREASTS WITH AVOCADO

Bored with chicken? Well, not with this recipe!

Ingredients

4 boneless and skinless chicken breasts

1 pink grapefruit

1 navel orange

lemon pepper seasoning

one whole avocado sliced

Directions

Marinate the chicken breasts overnight in a mixture of freshly squeezed grapefruit, lemons, and oranges. Sprinkle with lemon pepper. Coat a medium sized nonstick pan with cooking spray, place on medium heat. Cook through. take out of pan. Place the four slices of grapefruit in pan; cook until warm both sides. Top chicken with grapefruit slices and sliced fresh avocado.

ROASTED RED PEPPERS IN OLIVE OIL WITH GARLIC SHRIMP

Peppers are powerhouses packed with an incredible amount of vitamin c, giving you almost 300% of your RDA per serving. Shrimp is an excellent source of low fat, low calorie protein, which is also high in selenium. not to mention that everyone knows the wonders of olive and garlic.

Ingredients

4 large red peppers cut in half cold pressed extra virgin olive oil

2 tbsp. minced fresh basil

2 tsp balsamic vinegar

loaf of whole wheat bread, warmed to a light crisp in toaster oven

Fresh minced Italian herbs: oregano, parsley, sage, rosemary, and thyme

1 clove garlic

24 pieces of fresh shrimp, peeled and deveined

Directions

Rub the peppers with olive oil and place on cookie sheet. Broil on high for about three to five minutes or until you see the skin bubble up brownish black. Take the peppers out and place inside a plastic bag. This is a top chef cooking trick, which will help you to take the skin off more easily. When the peppers are cool, rub off skin. In a bowl, place the meat of the pepper; add vinegar and seasoning. Serve on a colorful plate with the bread, or place peppers on top of the bread. In a heated skillet add cooking spray and slightly brown garlic. Add the shrimp, cooking three to four minutes until pink in color. Serve with peppers and bread.

BAKED BLACKENED SALMON STEAKS WITH MANGO AND BLACK BEAN SALSA

Salmon is one of my favorite fish, as it's loaded with omega-3 fat, which is great for our hair, skin, and nails, and helps to fight off cancer.

The fruit in the salsa adds a kick of sweetness and is loaded with vitamin C. The black beans add fiber and are rich in antioxidants.

Ingredients

1 large mango, pitted and diced into 1/2 inch pieces

1 kiwi, peeled and diced

1 can of black beans, rinsed and drained

1/4 cup of cilantro, chopped

2 scallions, sliced tsp honey

dash of sea salt

dash of cayenne pepper

2 tbsp. salt-free blackening seasoning

1 lime, squeezed with juice set aside

4 salmon steaks, 4 ounces each

Directions

Heat oven to 350 degrees to make the salsa, in a mixing bowl, toss the first nine ingredients with half of the lime juice. Set the salsa aside. Place salmon steaks on a cooking tray. drizzle the remaining juice over the fi sh.

Sprinkle both sides with the blackening seasoning. Bake until cooked through, about fifteen to twenty minutes.

VIP FIT TIP: Always choose wild fish, never farmed. Farmed fish have higher levels of mercury and may even be toxic.

SUCCULENT AND EXOTIC ASIAN LETTUCE WRAPS

Bold flavors, crunchy vegetables, cool and crispy lettuce combined for delicious, hands-on meals! in addition, they're especially healthy. For lunch, add 1/2 cup cooked brown rice or a whole-grain roll for your complex carb. if you make this for dinner, eat without the carb.

Ingredients

at least 16 Boston bib or butter lettuce leaves

1 pound lean ground turkey

1 large onion chopped

2 cloves fresh garlic minced

1 tbsp. low sodium soy sauce

1/4 cup hoisin sauce

1 tbsp. rice wine vinegar

Asian pepper chili sauce

dash of cayenne pepper

1 can water chestnuts, rinsed and drained

1 bunch green onions, finely chopped

2 tsp dark Asian sesame oil

1/4 cup freshly minced parsley

1 tbsp. of chopped ginger

Directions

Rinse lettuce leaves, pat dry. in a medium skillet over high heat, brown the ground turkey and then set aside. In the same pan, cook the onion in the same pan, stirring frequently. add the garlic, soy sauce, hoisin sauce, ginger, vinegar, and chili pepper sauce to the onions and stir. add water chestnuts, green onions, sesame oil, and cook for about two minutes until the onions begin to wilt. Stir in cooked ground turkey. Serve meat filling in a large bowl with the lettuce leaves on the side. Fill each lettuce leaf with the meat mixture and eat like a burrito. Enjoy the contrast of the crisp coolness of the lettuce leaf with the hot rich meat mixture inside.

FILET MIGNON WITH LEMON PEPPER ASPARAGUS

Lean red meat is high in protein, and has vitamins and minerals, such as iron and vitamin B12, that fish or poultry don't contain. However, you should limit the amount of red meat that you eat. Aim for one time per week, or 3-4 times per month.

Ingredients

1 8-ounce lean fi let mignon

1 tsp ground black pepper

horseradish, to serve on the side

8 to 10 large spears of asparagus

Juice from one lemon

Black pepper

olive oil

Directions

Coat a nonstick pan with cooking spray. Heat to medium-high heat. Sprinkle pepper on both sides of steak. Place in pan, and sear on both sides. Cook to your liking. in a steamer, steam asparagus. Take out and drizzle with olive oil, squeeze the lemon on top, and then add a dash of freshly ground black pepper.

ASIAN TURKEY BURGERS

Here is a great recipe to liven up sometimes bland ground turkey. With garlic, parsley, ginger, and soy sauce, your burgers will be both delicious and packed with super food ingredients!

Ingredients

1 pound ground turkey

1 clove of garlic, finely minced

1/4 cup minced onion

3 tbsp. chopped fresh parsley

2 tbsp. Worcestershire sauce

2 tbsp. minced green bell pepper

1 tbsp. low sodium soy sauce

1 tbsp. cold water

1 tbsp. grated fresh ginger

1/4 tsp coarsely ground pepper

2 cloves of garlic crushed

Directions

Combine all ingredients in a big bowl and mix together until they're well combined. divide into three equal portions, and form into burgers about 3/4 inch thick.

Spray a skillet with nonstick cooking spray, and place over medium-high heat. cook the burgers for about five minutes per side until done through. Top with freshly sliced tomatoes and cold crisp lettuce.

CARIBBEAN SHRIMP AND MANGO SALAD

Ingredients

1 lb. of medium shrimp peeled and deveined

2 cloves garlic, finely chopped

2 tbsp. cold Pressed extra virgin olive oil

1 15 ounce can of black beans, rinsed and drained

1/4 cup red onion, halved and then thinly sliced

1/2 cup of fresh lime and lemon juice, mixed together

dash of allspice

6 cups of mixed greens

Directions

Cook shrimp with garlic in oil in skillet over medium low heat, not allowing the oil to smoke. Remove, and place in a large bowl. Add all other ingredients except the salad, tossing to coat. Then, just before serving, gently toss with the mixed greens.

Pre-bedtime Snack

- Small tin of tuna, rinsed, with a touch of fat free mayo and relish

- Two hard-boiled eggs with yokes removed, dashed with white pepper

- Small fat-free snack-size cottage cheese with strawberries and blueberries

- Chunks of cantaloupe wrapped in Prosciutto

- Four medium size precooked shrimp, dipped in cocktail sauce

Protein Shake Recipes

APPLE PIE À LA MODE PROTEIN SHAKE

Just like Mom used to make, but without the fat and calories!

Ingredients

    8 ounces of cold water

    1 scoop of Vanilla Protein Powder

    dash of cinnamon

    organic apple flavor extract

    3 ice cubes

    2 tbsp. Cool Whip Free

Directions

Pour water into blender, then protein powder, dash of cinnamon, and apple flavor extract. Blend on high for one minute. Then add ice, blend on high for one minute more. Pour into glass, top with cook Whip, and add another dash of cinnamon.

BEAUTIFUL BERRY BLAST PROTEIN SHAKE

Get a blast of antioxidant vitamin c, which is great for your immune system, plus gives you a super glow to your skin and helps to clear your complexion.

Ingredients

8 ounces of cold water

1 scoop of Vanilla Protein Powder,

Whipped vanilla flavor

1 cup of blueberries, strawberries, raspberries, and blackberries

3 ice cubes

2 tbsp. of cool Whip Free

a few extra berries to put on top of whipped cream

one sprig of mint

Directions

Pour cold water into blender. Put protein powder and berries into blender, blend on high for one minute. Add ice cubes, and then blend on high for one minute. Pour into glass, top with cool Whip and top with a few fresh berries and a spring of mint.

SUPER BANANA SPLIT PROTEIN SHAKE

Banana splits are my all-time favorite dessert! here is a healthy version that gives you all the different flavors and tastes of a banana split, without the unnecessary calories, carbs, or sugar.

Ingredients

8 ounces of water

one scoop of Vanilla Protein Powder,

half of one banana, or small banana

Few chunks of fresh pineapple

one maraschino cherry and a touch of its juice for that

added "wow" factor, or fresh cherries, your choice

3 cubes of ice

Directions

Blend on high and enjoy!

GERMAN CHOCOLATE CAKE PROTEIN SHAKE

There is nothing richer or dreamier than the combination of dark chocolate and the tropical scent of coconut. Another one of my favorite desserts, but this recipe will keep you lean while keeping you satisfied.

Ingredients

8 ounces of cold water

1 scoop chocolate protein shake

coconut candy Bar

1 tbsp. of coconut oil

1 tbsp. of coconut flakes

3 ice cubes

Blend and enjoy!

KEY LIME PIE PROTEIN SHAKE

I live in Miami, so when I get the chance to visit the Florida Keys, I stock up on fresh limes, which I use when I make this zesty and tangy shake.

Ingredients

8 ounces of cold water

1 scoop Vanilla Protein Shake

Juice of one fresh lime

1/4 cup of low-fat half and half

3 ice cubes

2 graham crackers, crushed up and placed in a dish

Directions

Blend all ingredients on high, except the graham crackers. Wet rim of the glass with water, then dip into crushed graham crackers. Pour in protein shake mixture.

Enjoy!

EXOTIC CHAI TEA PROTEIN SHAKE

This is a delicate blend of black tea, a touch of skim milk, ginger, and spices.

Ingredients

8 ounces of cold chai tea

dash of cinnamon

dash of ground ginger

1 scoop of BSN's lean dessert Protein Powder, Whipped Vanilla Flavor

1/4 cup low fat half and half

3 ice cubes

Directions

Blend on high speed and enjoy.

COOKIES AND CREAM PROTEIN SHAKE

An old-fashioned favorite reinvented with none of the guilt and a ton of health benefits.

Ingredients

8 ounces of cold water

one scoop of cookies and cream Flavored Protein Powder

or

one scoop Vanilla protein shake

1/4 cup cool Whip lite

3 chocolate wafer cookies

Directions

Add water to blender, add protein powder, and blend on medium speed until thoroughly mixed. Then add in cool Whip, ice cubes and blend for about half a minute. add cookie wafers and blend again for about fifteen seconds.

Pour and enjoy!

ISLAND PINA COLADA PASSION

Send your taste buds into instant vacation mode with this tropical cooler.

Ingredients

8 ounces of water

1 scoop of BSN's lean dessert Protein Powder, Whipped Vanilla Flavor

1/4 cup of fresh pineapple, cut into chunks

1 tbsp. of coconut oil

Directions

Add water to blender, then add protein powder, ice cubes, pineapple chunks, and coconut oil. Whip on high until thoroughly blended. Pour and enjoy!

CHOCOLATE COVERED CHERRY PROTEIN SHAKE

What can be more irresistible, juicy, and luscious than a dark chocolate-covered cherry? Well, this protein shake, of course!

Ingredients

8 ounces of cold water

1 scoop of chocolate protein shake

Handful of fresh cherries, pitted

1 tbsp. of maraschino cherry juice (or you can opt for fresh-pitted cherries)

3 ice cubes

Directions

Pour cold water into blender. add protein powder, cherries, and ice. Blend on high.

Pour and enjoy!

VIP Juice Recipes

Juicing is a quick, easy, and efficient way to give your body the vitamins and daily serving of fruits and vegetables that it need in one glass. Think about it, raw fruits and vegetables are living things! So, if you want more energy, eat more of them. They are fresh, and haven't had their nutritional content diluted and diminished through cooking, processing, or being preserved. The more "alive" and "living" fresh fruits and vegetables you eat, the more alive you will feel and the more energy you will have! When you incorporate such a blessing of nutrients into your food plan through juicing, you will enjoy heightened spiritual awareness, plus relaxation of the mind, body and soul. The combinations of fruit and vegetables are endless. Here are some of my favorite juice and veggie blends that will get and keep your body happy and humming. Cheers to your health!

BRAIN BOOSTER

Here is a juice to stimulate the other 90% of our brains that we don't use. This nutrient-rich, wide spectrum juice will feed the brain into razor-sharp mode. The benefits of drinking this juice are better memory, acuity of mind, and a clearer head with no more morning brain fog. Put that bounce back into your step with this super juice!

  1 pear

  1 apple

  1 orange

  1 carrot stick

  1 stalk celery

  1 beet

  a small chunk of ginger

Juice all ingredients and pour over ice. Drink immediately to get the best benefits.

PAIN-BE-GONE JUICE

To alleviate aches and pains, lessen irritation, and reduce inflammation, it's essential to detoxify the blood stream with super cleansing fruits and vegetables in a juice form for higher and quicker absorption. This juice is more than delicious, as it is also therapeutic and helps in the healing processes. if you are waking up feeling stiff and suffer from arthritis, then this is a perfect blend of juices.

    1 lemon

    1 orange

    1 pear

    1 apple

    1 large carrot stick

    a cup of fresh dark pitted cherries

Juice all ingredients and pour over ice. Drink immediately to get the best benefits.

ATHLETE'S DELIGHT

If you want to start looking, feeling, and performing like an athlete, then you must fuel up like one! Enjoy this "lightning bolt" of energy in a glass that will help you to have more speed, agility, endurance, stamina, and quickness.

1 cup of watermelon

1 granny smith apple

1 lemon

1 cup of pineapple

2 stalks celery

1 cup of cantaloupe

a small chunk of ginger

a bunch of parsley

Juice all ingredients and pour over ice. Drink immediately to get the best benefits.

ANTI-AGING JUICE RECIPE

Get a more youthful glow to your entire aura with this anti-aging super juice! Yes, antioxidants can help you turn back the clock!

a handful of blueberries and strawberries

a small bunch of parsley

a healthy bunch of spinach and kale

1 kiwi

1 tomato

1 lemon

3 broccoli florets

1 apple

2 apricots

1 carrot

1 red pepper

2 beets

Juice all ingredients and pour over ice. Drink immediately to get the best benefits.

FULL BODY CLEANSE AND BLOOD DETOXIFIER JUICE

Beets are the main focus of this juice because they're a powerful cleanser of the blood, kidneys, and liver. The garlic has doses of potassium, copper, iron, phosphorus, and iron, and will ward off any oncoming cold. The radish is a diuretic, cleanser, and disinfectant, which can help wash away the toxins accumulated in the kidneys.

1 garlic clove

4 beets

3 celery stalks

3 pineapple chunks

a healthy amount of spinach

1 apple

1 piece of fresh ginger

1 tomato

4 radishes

Juice all ingredients and pour over ice. Drink immediately to get the best benefits.

SEXY HAIR, SKIN, AND NAILS SIPPER

This beauty blend helps those of us who suffer from dull skin, dry hair, and easy-to-chip nails. This decadent sipper will give your outward appearance a healthy boost with juice to glow, radiate, and shine. Your skin will look brighter, your hair will be thicker and more lustrous, and your nails stronger. Being beautiful never tasted so good! Aloe is moisture-rich, and cucumber is high in silica, which is a mineral that fortifies connective tissue, thus increasing skin elasticity. Parsley promotes firming of the skin, and sweet potato is an excellent source of beta-carotene, which will give you a great complexion.

1 full aloe leaf

1 cucumber

a handful of grapes

1 pomegranate

a cup of blueberries and strawberries

1 sweet potato

a few leaves of romaine lettuce

a snip of parsley and parsnips

Juice all ingredients and pour over ice. Drink immediately to get the best benefits.

VIPs, so you can see just how important, and delicious, it is to fuel your mind, body and spirit like a VIP!

For more, make sure you www.JNLVIP.com and join our community of other like-minded women who have made their VIP Power a Top Priority! Your first month is only $1! You have nothing to lose, but excuses! Let's do this!

Chapter 7

VIP MONEY MANAGEMENT & FINANCIAL SUCCESS

Buckle Up VIPS! You are on the Super Highway to Financial Freedom

VIPS, let's talk about that "green back potato salad", those "frijoles", that cold-hard cash!

MY STORY SEEING MY MOM STRUGGLE FINANCIALLY:

I remember early in my childhood always hearing my mother say, "we can't afford that", "we don't have the money to buy that", "that's too expensive", or even "your father owes me money", or "because of your father, we are broke".

I remember her having to rely on my dad, who was pretty much absent from my life, except for when he would visit on weekends. She was financially dependent upon a man. I learned very early on, that this was not a good way to have your financial foundation set up. My father often never came through. My mother had to go to court many times in an effort to enforce him to pay his child support. It usually got ugly.

So, as a young girl, I learned first-hand, that it was never a good idea to rely on a man as your main source of income, financial security, or financial well-being.

I never wanted to be in the desperate situations I witnessed my mom suffer through many times. I knew that I wanted to work, earn money, and then make that money work for me.

MEET ONE OF MY CLIENTS, MELISSA:

Melissa was on a roll in terms of her financial success. She was working in her dream job making a good solid living, with hopes of being promoted which would increase her annual salary. Then, she met Billy. Billy was in between jobs, so he asked if he could live with her for a few weeks. This was a short term arrangement that would dissolve when he got a job and back on his feet. A few weeks, turned into 18 months. During one and half year time period, Melissa paid all of the bills, including all of their entertainment, grocery shopping, and living expenses. Not only did Billy drain her bank account, his empty promises drained her emotionally and physically. She started showing up late for work, and eventually got demoted. She finally reclaimed and unleashed her VIP power and kicked Billy out. She learned a very important lesson from that experience, however, although the lesson was significant, it was also very costly. It took her years to get back on track financially, and to build back up her confidence to a level that would allow her to gain a high paying, high level job.

She vowed never to take care of a man, no matter how deeply in love she was with him, and to set up a savings, and retirement fund.

Do you feel my pain from my mom's story? Can you relate to Melissa's story? Well, let's crack this money code and set you up for financial success, instead of money misery!

By the end of this chapter, you will know how to earn, how to save and how to make your money work for you!

EARN MONEY by WORKING

In order to have money, you got to earn it! So, make sure you are working at least one job. Yes, I said at least one job. I also highly suggest having a side hustle, or a freelance position that you can do on your off or down time.

EARN MONEY by Liquidating What You Are Not Using

Remember that designer handbag that you purchased 5 years ago? Remember how much you loved it then, but fast forward to today and it has lost its importance in your life? Well, list it on eBay, or The Real, to turn that useless stash into cash! Look at your closet, and list what you are not using, swap it out for cash. There are many people who have turned their full time profession into selling on EBay.

SAVE MONEY:

It's time to get serious. Yes, you can save money, I have heard it time and time again. "I don't have any money to save", as you hold a cup of Starbucks coffee in your hand, rocking designer sunglasses, with a high-end designer bag dangling from your wrist. First of all, you should not be purchasing a $3,000 dollar handbag if you don't even know how to earn that much to put into that purse or wallet. Don't hate the messenger! I'm just stating the truth!

Start by taking a good look at your lifestyle, and then cut down all the frivolous spending.

The 50/30/20 Rule

It varies from person to person on how much you should save. However, a basic rule of thumb is that you should pull out 20% of your income and put that into your savings. You should budget 50% of your income towards your necessities. Now, this is the maximum number. You can always aim to budget a lesser amount. Then the other 30% goes towards discretionary items.

STOP IMPULSE BUYING:

Have you ever went out, and ended up buying something you didn't even plan on buying? And when you got it home, you had a guilty feeling? This is called "Buyer's Remorse". It's a horrible feeling! Even worse of a feeling if you can't return the item. If you can't trust yourself, then don't take your credit card out shopping. Plain and simple. Remember, Dora the Explorer? Well, repeat after me: Swiper No Swiping!

SPEND BELOW YOUR MEANS, BUY WITHIN YOUR MEANS.

Just because you can afford it, doesn't mean you have to buy it!

> *JNL, I really want to earn more money, and manifest more abundance into my life! But, no matter what I do, I never have enough money, and I always spend more than I should! Help!*

You could be suffering from having a limited mindset about money. You need to retrain your brain to see money making opportunities, to remove all subconscious blocks to money, and to also retrain your mindset into accepting and allowing prosperity into your life. Please click here to enjoy a FREE Guided Meditation on Abundance to help you break through to abundance:

https://www.youtube.com/watch?v=hXcy7GbwFac&t=8
28s

INVEST

LIMITED MINDSETS ABOUT MONEY

COST VS VALUE

QUICK VIP MONEY MAGAGEMENT TOOL-THERE'S AN APP FOR THAT!

There are so many cool apps out there that help you budget and save! I suggest these following:

- Acorns
- YNAB
- Pocket Guard
- Personal Capital.
- Wally
- Mint.com
- Dollarbird
- Mvelopes

GOT A DREAM? THEN OPEN UP A DREAM ACCOUNT TO FUND YOUR DREAM

Ever wanted to go to Hawaii? Or take a trip to Bali? Or afford that second piece of rental real estate? To purchase that designer bag? To drive that super sports car?

Well, YES YOU CAN, Only if you can afford it by saving up and still living within your means.

Every pay check, strive to put a certain percentage away into your Dream Fund. It's so much fun when you see your money grow in honor of your life's goals and dreams.

"Out of sight, out of mind" is the approach you should have regarding the money that you set aside for your dream. Don't touch it! Don't loan it out to a broke friend! Keep your eye on the prize.

FICO SCORE/CREDIT SCORES:

Pay your bills on time. Your bill payment history is 35% of your FICO score.

So, keep your credit spotless. If you have bad credit, enroll into a credit repair program immediately!

VIP TIP: CHECK YOUR BANK ACCOUNT DAILY! Don't turn a blind eye to it. Your account could have a "leak" in it, with a sneaky automated charge you didn't even agree to. So as Biggy Smalls says, "keep your mind on your money, and your money on your mind!

DIAMOND RULES OF VIP FINACINAL POWER:

1. Always have access to a six- eight month emergency fund
2. Be out of credit card debt
3. Contribute to your 401 K
4. Have a ROTH IRA if you qualify for it.
5. Keep your personal and professional finances separate. Don't ever rob Peter to pay Paul.

RESOURCES:

Upfront Disclaimer: I am not an attorney, therefore I encourage you to seek out a local attorney to make sure you are filling out your corporation incorporation application correctly. If you can't afford an attorney, you can use affordable legal services like "Legal Zoom", as it offers budget friendly legal services and support.

SET UP AN LC AND THEN APPLY FOR A PROPER NET 30 ACCOUNT

Setup your LLC correctly from the get-go. This will ensure that you have a strong start to being a successful entrepreneur. Then once your LLC is established, you can apply for a NET-30 account.

Here is a list of NET-30 Accounts you can apply for:

Summa Office Supplies

Quill

Grainger

Uline

Office Depot

WHY IS IT IMPORTANT TO WORK WITH BUSINESSNESS THAT OFFER A NET 30 ACCOUNT?

A net-30 account is one that extends you 30 days to pay the bill in full after you have purchased products. It's vendor credit that allows you to buy now and pay later. This will help you to build business credit, and that's always a plus!

ASSETS VS LIABILITIES

In its simplest form, your balance sheet can be divided into two categories: **assets** and **liabilities**. **Assets** are the items your company owns that can provide future economic benefit. **Liabilities** are what you owe other parties. In short, **assets** put money in your pocket, and **liabilities** take money out!

LIST OF ASSETS VS LIST OF LIABILITIES:

Here is a list of ASSETS that MAKE you MONEY

1. Cash
2. Inventory
3. accounts receivable
4. land
5. buildings
6. equipment

Here is a List of LIABILITIES that Cost You Money

1. money that must be paid
2. services that must be performed
3. Rent

VIP FINANCIAL GOLDEN RULE OF SUCCESS:

A successful company has more **assets** than **liabilities**, meaning it has the resources to fulfill its obligations

VIP FUN-WORK:
LIST YOUR ASSETS BELOW:

_____

_____

_____

_____

_____

_____

LIST YOUR LIABILITIES BELOW:

_____

_____

_____

_____

_____

_____

EXPLAIN BELOW HOW YOU CAN DIAL DOWN ON THE UNECCESSARY EXPENSES?

_____

_____

_____

VIP MONEY WISDOM: IF YOU DON'T TAKE CARE OF YOUR MONEY, IT WILL LEAVE YOU!

VIP Money Tip: If you don't take care of your money, it will leave you-straight out of your bank account!

EXIT STRATEGY-We all want to have the dream life, the dream car, the dream home and the dream job. But I can tell you this, there will come a time in your life, that you will want to stop working completely, and retire in order to enjoy the best years of your life. So, you need to make sure that you are saving religiously so that you have a retirement fund in place.

Let's do the math:

At what age do you want to retire?

How much money do you want to have per year?

For example, if you want to retire when you are 55, and women typically live to be 75 years old, and you need $100,000 dollars per year to live the lifestyle that you want, you will need 2 million dollars. Now, that's a wake-up call! So, let's get to saving!

ADDITIONAL NOTES:

_____

_____

_____

_____

_____

_____

_____

_____

_____

_____

_____

_____

_____

_____

_____

_____

_____

_____

Chapter 8

MAINTAINING YOUR VIP STATUS!

Getting to the Top is Easy.
Staying there is another story.

-JNL

How to Crack the Code to Being Persistent and Consistent

One thing for sure, everybody is hot and fired up right out of the gate. Everyone has a big talk game, and they show some kind of action, but they tend to fade out really quick after a few weeks. You see, we all want the dream, but not many of us are willing to work for it. We all want the appearance of winning, without living the disciplined lifestyle required to achieve and maintain it. We all want the fame and glory, but the problem is that we want these things without the sacrifice that precedes it.

In this chapter I am going to give you a mental adjustment so that you can get your mind-set right to get your VIP status on tight!

Many of my VIP clients have called me "The Mind-Cracker", or even "The Fitness Whisperer" for my ability to transform a meek and mild mouse into a roaring lion. This chapter will be powerful, potent, and extremely effective in making sure you maintain your new VIP identity and VIP status.

Be Clear on Your Why

When CEO's, entrepreneurs, and business owners fizzle out, it's mainly because they lose focus of their "WHY".

Answer the following questions below and be clear in your answers!

1. Why did you start your success journey?

2. Why did you want to be a VIP in the first place?

3. Why do you want more out of life?

4. Why did you take positive action from the start?

5. Why did you yearn and earn for more in your career?

6. Why did you want to elevate your status from follower to a leader?

Keep Your "Why in your Eye"!

Once you become crystal clear on your why, KEEP IT IN FRONT OF YOUR EYE! Set visual reminders up around you to constantly trigger you in a good way to keep going, and to never give up.

You know the saying "out of sight, out of mind?" Well, I like to say, "In sight, in mind". So, make a list of your WHY's, and keep them in front of your eyes as a constant reminder.

Go Peak to Peak

When you are hot, you are hot. When you are not, you're not. So, keep your calendar peppered and sprinkled with WINS! Once you hit one goal, and it's completed, you should have 10 more lined up on your calendar.

I had a client, and she had a goal of winning a fitness competition. She trained all year for it. She competed, and placed 6th which was not bad for a beginner. However, she paid so much attention to that one goal, that she failed to set up other PEAKS to climb and conquer after her competition. She went from a Peak (her fitness competition), to a valley. Sadly enough, she stayed in that "valley". She never set any bigger goals.

Meet Nancy on the other hand. She set up some goals to be the top earner in her company, to start a new side hustle, to enter a marathon, and to then go on a charity mission trip/vacation at the end of the year. She went from "peak" to "peak" and was on a success role. She didn't have time to even hit a "valley" as after she crushed one goal, she had the other goals right on her calendar to focus on.

The take away here is, get your calendar out, and start planning your "Peaks", so you will never be in a "valley" for too long, as you can lose momentum and drive.

How do you plan to make sure you have Peak to Peak to go to in your life?

Schedule It: Don't prioritize your schedule. Instead schedule your priorities. Remember, if it's not on your schedule, it won't happen. VIPS don't let life just happen, instead they make things happen in life.

List below how you plan on making sure to always put your priorities on your schedule:

_____

_____

_____

_____

_____

_____

_____

Look the Part-ALWAYS! Be pulled together and polished! Do you ever see Dolly Parton out of her wig and makeup? Do you ever see Beyoncé looking ratchet? No. Be married and committed to always being on point, polished, pulled together and in control of your life.

List below your actions steps on how you plan on always looking like the VIP that you are:

_____

_____

_____

_____

_____

_____

_____

Ignore Your Feelings-This is the only time you will ever hear me say this! It's your job to be fabulous and fierce. Yes, you may be tired. Yes, you may not feel like it. Yes, you may not want to go. But your feelings have nothing to do with you being consistent. It's time to toughen up, and show up! So, get up, dress up, show up, kick butt and never give up! Get out there and be fabulous, like it's your job.

<u>Be consistent in showing up:</u> VIP's never flake out, cancel or not show up to events or meetings they have committed to attending. Their word is their word.

Con artists and scammers give empty promises. Not VIPs. If you know you can't attend, don't RSVP. Confirm to the other parties involved that you will be there, and you will be showing up on time. Stick to your word. Have strong decision-making muscles. Guard your reputation by only writing checks with your mouth that you know your actions can cash in, and not bounce!

Remember that new identity in Chapter 1 that you have made a commitment to becoming? Well, that's who you have become, not just because you said it, but because your actions are in alignment with your identity.

TOP 10 COMMANDMENTS VIP CONSISTANCIES:

1. You are on time
2. You are polished
3. You "look the part"
4. You are prepared
5. You are organized!
6. You have a positive mindset-
7. No more negative conversations
8. You are committed
9. You are consistent
10. You are productive

Remember when you made a goal, but only fizzled out after 2 weeks, and how horrible you felt? Well, don't let that ever happen again! Maintain your VIP status, be proud of yourself, and make if fun!

Chapter 9

ROCK VIP PRIDE! SHINE BRIGHT!

VIPS! You made it! You are consistent. You are showing up for yourself, and others that are also invested in your wellbeing. You are wildly successful, and you are shining bright. Are you feeling fabulous? Keep it going, and never give up!

Now this is the real fun part.

VALIDATE YORUSELF

One major success lifestyle hack that a VIP capitalizes on is that they validate themselves, instead of waiting for validation from others. So, let's set up your reward system.

Write down small micro-rewards daily! Experience the joy of when you cross it off your VIP to-do.

Your brain is going to get that surge of dopamine, and it's going to feel the pleasure of you completing tasks, both big and small. Therefore, you will be experiencing a constant influx of motivation.

Aim to condition yourself. Train your nuero-pathways so your mind is hard-wired to link pleasure to crushing your goals. Again, you

are "hard-wiring" yourself for success. There is no more struggling. There is no more "I want to be successful, but I can't seem to be consistent." You are ending the "civil war" between wanting it and then actually working for it. You are now linking pain to not taking positive action and linking pleasure to taking action.

You are doing it, and its sticking, for good!

The next step is to set up some big rewards for when you achieve larger goals.

I call this your VIP Bucket List- The Top List of Things You Really Want to Do!

Some examples can be:

A Girls Trip to an Exotic Location

Redoing Your Home/Home Renovations

Enjoying that Designer Handbag-that you actually can fill up with your financial success

Fabulous Dinner out on the town, all dressed to the nines.

A Solo Trip for Yourself

Buying that Diamond Ring/Bracelet/Necklace for yourself

WHAT ARE YOUR PERSONAL VIP BUCKET LIST GOALS?

Write and share below! Remember, nothing is too big or too daring! Dream Big!

1.

2.

3.

4.

5.

DON'T HATE! APPRECIATE!

"Haters don't really hate you. They hate themselves, because you are a reflection of what they wish to be."-JNL

It's true: women who are happy are not hating. Plain and simple. A VIP woman is so focused on her goals that she doesn't have time to be checking on everyone else. Stay in your VIP Lane, and keep your eyes on your side of the street.

One of my clients had big goals, but she also had big problems focusing because she seemed to be always trying to out-shine and out-do her friend. She wasted so much time trying to "keep up with the Joneses" that she lost her passion and purpose, and she got off track with her success. I told her to get back on track, but this time, to keep her "horse-blinders" on and to stay focused on her goals.

She was able to maintain her drive, excitement, and enthusiasm for her VIP lifestyle because she brought her focus back to her goals. She stopped trying to outdo others. Believe me, this makes all the difference! Just think about the time that is wasted checking in and up on others. Redirect that time and energy back onto your life and goals

VIPS CELEBRATE OTHER VIPS

I have had the great honor of working with some high profile, extremely successful CEO's, business owners, leaders and powerful people. They share many personality traits that makes them successful. A major one is that they are never jealous and always giving others compliments. . They actually take the time to acknowledge the successes and accomplishments of others. This astounded me. Don't be stuck up! Instead, stand up for your other fellow VIP's that you admire. Remember the law of karma? What you put out comes back to you! So, applaud others successes and the same will come back to you.

Be willing to celebrate the VIP success of those around you. As I always say, "there's a lot of room at the top."

We don't compete with one another. Instead, we complete one another.

A VIP woman knows how to share the "limelight" and the "red carpet".

And as the saying goes, "Just because one candle shines, it doesn't dim the light of the other candles." In the contrary, the candles together shine brighter. It's just more winning, more abundance, more prosperity, and more shine for all! So, shine baby shine!

Chapter 10

UNLEASH YOUR VIP POWER

"If you have found your power, unleash it and let others light their candles in it!"

-JNL

Now that you have RECLAIMED your VIP POWER, it is time to UNLEASH IT!

Remember if you don't use it, you will lose it! And if you don't use it, you might as well not have even read the last 9 Chapters!

You have made it to this pivotal point in your personal and professional life, and it's time to UNLEASH your VIP POWER!

The word UNLEASH is powerful! Just look it up in the dictionary!

To release from; to set loose to pursue or run at will.

Another word for unleash is to "activate". Its meaning in the dictionary is to make active; cause to function or act.

So, as you can see, this entire chapter is dedicated to you TAKING ACTION!

Why is this so important? Actually, it's the most important aspect of your new VIP lifestyle.

If you fail to take action, then you will stay stuck in the old, frustrated and unfulfilled version of yourself.

Not Taking Action is the Biggest Mistake:

I have been a transformational Coach, fitness artist and master trainer for close to 20 years. Failing to unleash your power, not activating your power, and not taking action with your power are all of the major reasons why people don't achieve what they want in life.

You see, it's so easy to learn what you should do. But doing it is a whole different issue. The challenge, the difficult part, and the stage where many get stuck is in taking that next step.

In this chapter, you have all of the keys to VIP success, and this is where we TURN THE KEYS TO UNLEASH, ACTIVATE, and TAKE ACTION with your VIP POWER in all areas of your life!

FOCUS

"Be a Laser, in a World of Flash Lights"-JNL

In a world where we are being constantly distracted, and our attention is being bombarded, it is very challenging to stay focused, and to stay the course.

Here are some VIP hacks to help you stay focused.

Remember why you started: This is essential in your ability to stay focused and never give up.

Have Intentions: Be intentional, in all things that you do. Ask yourself "What are my intentions" with every project and daily activity that you do. This empowering question will help you to maintain your focus.

Be Mindful. Always consider all circumstances in the entire situation. Be mindful of yourself, and all that are being blessed by your new VIP power.

Think Things Through: Think of your actions as a chess move, on a chess board. Always think 10 steps ahead.

Shiny object Syndrome: Let's call Shiny Object Syndrome SOS for short.

Okay, let's face it. We all get distracted sometimes. But when it becomes so bad that you may feel like a "gerbil on a wheel" going nowhere fast.

Here are some telltale signs to see if you are suffering from SOS.

If you find it hard to wrap up projects, or you sometimes abandon projects and never finish them, letting them hang in the balance undone.

You have bad planning, and sometimes just jump into projects as easily as you jump out of them.

You are just throwing money at problems and also keep changing and switching projects. You spend "startup money" on a project, but don't finish it, because you got distracted and lured into another "amazing opportunity."

You may have so many balls up in the air, that you are confusing yourself and also your team.

How to overcome SOS:

Let ideas "marinate" before committing to them.

Mastermind with your team. Get their input and feedback before you launch a new project.

Make sure you set clear long-term goals for each project. It's all fun at first, and then reality kicks in. Don't jump ship mid project just to start another one. Have your long-term goals in site.

Eliminate Distractions: Always remove and avoid distractions. Why set yourself up for failure, if you can on the other hand set yourself up for success. Why do you think award winning athletes go away to a secluded training camp before a big match, competition or fight? The reason is so they can be focused and not distracted.

Think about your next big business deal, your big financial transaction, and your up and coming projects as a "fight, match or competition". You don't have time to be lured into other people's problems, or to be enticed into committing to obligations you have no business dealing with anyways. It's okay to seclude yourself, to have alone planning time, and to get prepared in solitude.

> *When an ordinary person has laser like focus, they unlock the VIP inside of them and become extraordinary! –JNL*

VIP TIP & ACTION STEP:

Once a day, turn off all distractions. Turn off your phone, your TV, and your laptop or tablet. Make a list of the top goals you must complete, and give them a deadline. And then map out some quick tasks you must do in order to achieve these goals. This will help you stay laser focused!

Live in Purpose:

When you live in true purpose, it will be extremely easy to stay focused. If projects, and opportunities arise, but are not in alignment with your purpose, it will be very easy for you to turn them down and not get lured by them. So, stay in your purpose!

> *"JNL Help me! I have so many things to do! And I get overwhelmed that it is hard for me to focus! What can I do?"*

Great question! Learning how to focus is an art form. You must focus on "the bullseye" of all goals. The "bullseye" are the priorities of each goal. So, focus on the center, the main priorities, and then worry about the outlying rings of the goals later. Always focus and address the most important steps first of each goal and project. This will not only help you be more effective and efficient in your work, but it will also save your sanity!

BUIDLING A GOOD TEAM

> *"You are only as good as the people you surround yourself with."*

Now that you are ready to rock your VIP power, you need to build a solid trust worthy team that you can count on.

As you recruit your VIP Team, keep these pointers in mind:

First you need to know how small or big you want your team.

Have the roles of each player defined clearly.

Don't micro-manage.

Aim to always hire the best.

Once you have a team, don't run a one-woman-show. Get your team members involved.

Know your team members in and out. Be very aware of their strengths & weaknesses.

Always engage in team building exercises.

Be an Excellent Leader to Your Team! Be sure you are leading them to a group victory.

QUESTION: "JNL, I have a great team, however one of my staff members is always trying to outdo me, speak louder than me, point out things that I may have missed, and almost wants to be the boss lady in charge. It's a definite power struggle. What should I do?"

ANSWER: If you feel that one of your team members are competing for your spot, then pull them aside and let them know how you feel. If you feel that there is a power struggle, and things are not meshing, and you have given them many chances to change their behavior, feel free to let this person go. As I say many times, don't try to give CPR to a dead situation.

DON'T FIZZLE OUT LIKE DAY OLD 7UP!

Everybody is hot out of the gate. It's all fun and games at the start, then reality kicks in.

It's not always unicorns and rainbows when you are your own boss. When you are an entrepreneur, you don't get to clock out and clock in. You are on 24/7. You have to solve problems, deal with a variety of different situations at any given moment, and it can be extremely challenging. Don't fizzle out like day old 7-Up soda.

It's really survival of the fittest. You got to be strong and relentless on the pursuit of success.

You got to be as tough as nails. Being a VIP is not for the faint of heart. But if you have the right mental attitude, stay strong, and never give up, believe in your value and worth, you can and will be the best VIP ever.

Busy VS Productive

VIPS are PRODUCTIVE! Not Just Busy!

This is huge! Let's get this very clear: There is a vast difference between being productive and being just down right busy. Being busy is just someone who is doing a lot, and may not get the results that they want. They might not even have clear and concise goals. They are just spinning their wheels with no traction.

A productive, effective and efficient person is one who is focused, and is fueled by purpose.

What makes the difference between the busy person vs the productive person is the end result.

The busy person doesn't get results. They just burn out and get exhausted. While the productive person gets results.

So, don't mistake busy for getting results.

Once you are able to master being productive, the next step is being efficient. Aim to get more results with less work. That is not being lazy. This is being smart! Aim to work smarter, not harder. VIPs don't waste their time or energy. They make sure that they get the results that they are after, without expending energy they don't need to waste.

DON'T COMPARE YOUR CHAPTER 1 TO SOMEONES CHAPTER 20!

Success comes in many stages. So, if you are just starting out, you cannot compare your Chapter 1 to someone's Chapter 20. Learn from those VIPs who have gone before you and who have paved the way. Don't be envious of them. It has taken them countless years to get to where they are in life.

KEEP EVOLVING

Okay VIPS! Now you are off of that desperate downward spiral, and now climbing the upward spiral of success, you must keep evolving!

Every next level of your life will demand a different, better version of you. So, don't be afraid to grow, evolve, flourish, change, gain new talents, sharpen up your skills set, do more and be more. Continue on your personal and professional evolution! There is always more in you!

Remember, you can't be who you used to be and who you are going to be at the same time.

In order to stay moving forward you have to stop slipping back.

Let me state this very clear: You cannot live a VIP lifestyle if you continuously allow mediocrity to creep back into your life.

Action Steps:

- Seek out new empowerment programs

- Join an online coaching program that supports your new VIP lifestyle.Learn a New Skill

- Go through more executive training

- Explore your talents by using them!

- Say yes to that side hustle that will train you and open new doors for you

USE WHAT YOU GOT, RIGHT HERE, RIGHT NOW

A VIP never functions from a stance of scarcity or lack. They always believe they have enough in each stage of their journey of personal and professional excellence. They continue to build and grow on their current level of success. They never "want that" or "wish" they had that. They trust the journey and show up with gratitude.

May I urge you to see your life in abundance right now, and to use what you have!

Stop focusing on what you don't have, and focus on what you do have.

Powerful Metaphor of "The Cake"

Many of us are asking for a cake, when we already have all the ingredients. We have the flour, the sugar, the eggs, the milk and the butter. We have everything we need in order make this cake. But we have to shift our focus from "oh, I wish I had that cake" to "I am going to use all of the right ingredients to make the most beautiful cake".

Find joy in the creation of your goals, dreams and VIP lifestyle. Don't just focus on the end result. This is a journey, not a one-time event. It's a journey to be enjoyed!

So, use what you have. Be resourceful, and most importantly-BE GRATEFUL!

VIPS ARE NOT IMPRESSIONABLE & NOT EASILY INFLUENCED

One thing that I learned about studying and observing some of the most powerful, prolific and strongest leaders and game changers of today, is that they are not easily impressed. A strength they have is that they are not impressionable. They are not easily swayed.

They are the big dogs. They have seen big mansions, big yachts, luxury super cars, expensive watches and crazy vacations. They don't even flinch. They have seen people get rich, and go broke within the same year. They have seen many fall in love, get married, and divorced in a short period of time. They have seen many friends become multi-millionaires, but also suffer from depression and anxiety.

You see, as the saying goes, "all that glitters ain't gold." VIPs don't take things at face value, especially when we live in a society that is highly driven by controlled online content.

VIP Success Tip: Take everything with a grain of sand. Focus on yourself. Stay in your lane. And keep your eye on the prize.

In closing, it is time for you to activate your VIP Power, to unleash it and to share it with others!

Know that you are royal. You are a VIP. You have the power. You have had it all along. You now have RECLAIMED your VIP POWER, and you are READY TO UNLEASH IT!

For more info, please visit www.JenniferNicoleLee.com and if you are not already an valued VIP member, join our Online Coaching Community at www.JNLVIP.com to continue to grow and strengthen your VIP power!

ABOUT THE AUTHOR

Jennifer Nicole Lee is a top transformational coach, fitness artist, specialist in sports nutrition and supplementation, a master trainer, and the author of 16 books. Her passion is to empower others to increase the quality of their lives in all areas.. JNL lost over 80 lbs. after the birth of her children close to 2 decades ago, leading her to be one of the most highly sought-after wellness experts. She has dedicated her life's work to helping others achieve their wildest dreams and goals. For more, please visit
www.JenniferNicoleLee.com

To become a VIP member to her online coaching program, please sign up at www.JNLVIP.com

Made in the USA
Columbia, SC
03 September 2023

22362038R00112